Weather Satellites

A BLAISDELL BOOK
IN THE PURE
AND APPLIED SCIENCES

CONSULTING EDITOR   •   GORDON J. F. MacDONALD,
University of California

Weather Satellites

LESTER F. HUBERT   PAUL E. LEHR

● ● ● National Environmental Satellite Center

● BLAISDELL PUBLISHING COMPANY

A Division of Ginn and Company

Waltham, Massachusetts · Toronto · London

476

The use of satellites in meteorology is so new that few people, even professional meteorologists, appreciate the full implications of this new technology. Students and scientists in other fields must wonder why instruments carried hundreds of miles above all weather are preferred to those carried by balloons within the atmosphere.

The satellite itself, the measurement of meteorological parameters from far above the earth, and the techniques of recovering and using the data are largely unknown to those who do not work directly with the system. In this book we have attempted to bring to the reader an understanding of the basic reasons satellite data are so important to research and day-to-day forecasting. In addition, we have described the space system and the data reduction and utilization procedures as they exist today, and we have indicated how we believe they will evolve.

Weather satellites have given us a powerful technique for seeing the entire atmosphere at work. At the same time, the unique nature of the observations makes it difficult to extract information in the form of quantities usable to meteorologists. But even in the relatively short time these new data have been available, meteorologists have devised empirical methods for making direct use of the information. Research teams continue to develop techniques useful in daily weather work, and they are also uncovering heretofore unknown bits and pieces of information on the basic workings of atmospheric phenomena and the atmosphere as a whole.

This book explains the manner in which satellite observations are interpreted and speculates on how other types of data may be acquired from future satellite systems. The text thus represents a composite of research, plans, and speculation on the part of the authors and their colleagues in the meteorological community. The authors take full responsibility for their statements. However, they gratefully acknowledge the ideas made available to them in the published writings of the many meteorologists throughout the world who are working with the new set of problems brought to light in this space age of meteorology.

L. F. HUBERT   ·   P. E. LEHR

Contents

1. Weather Observing Enters the Space Age 1

2. Observing from Space 13

3. The First Five Years of Weather Satellites 29

4. Data Acquisition and Reduction 53

5. Satellite Data in Daily Forecasting 67

6. Use of Satellite Data in Research 81

7. The Future of Weather Satellites 99

Basic Books for More Information 118

Index 119

1

••••

Weather Observing

Enters the Space Age

On October 4, 1957, the space age opened with the spectacular announcement from Moscow that Sputnik I, the first man-made artificial moon, was orbiting the earth once every 96 minutes. January 31, 1958, witnessed the launching of Explorer I, the first United States satellite to be orbited successfully. From then until April 1, 1960, forty-four satellite launchings were attempted by both nations. Twenty were successful to varying degrees: some went into orbit but remained silent; some are still orbiting the earth or the sun; and the rest re-entered the earth's atmosphere where they either vaporized or were lost in the oceans.

• • • • • • •

April 1, 1960, is a day to remember in the history of meteorology. On that date TIROS I was launched, went into orbit, and sent to earth the first successful television pictures of clouds and landmarks. These pictures showed the clouds associated with a great storm system extending into the northeastern United States from southern Canada and the land area marking the St. Lawrence estuary. Meteorologists at the New Jersey read-out station who saw the first television pictures were overjoyed at the success. Here at last was a means of looking at the earth's cloud patterns, patterns which are natural weather maps. These cloud patterns are vastly different from the kind of maps the meteorologist is accustomed to using. The weather maps he normally uses show conditions which are measured or estimated from the ground or low in the atmosphere—weather conditions which cannot be detected directly by weather satellites. So while the satellite pictures give new information, their use also requires the development of new techniques relating this new source of information to the established sources and new methods for using the satellite data.

Why do we need weather satellites? What can they do that is not already being done? By observing weather on a scale not possible by any other means, the satellite has given the meteorologist a comprehensive view of the world's weather. This view is not only helping to answer some questions that have plagued the meteorologist, but it has also opened vast new areas of research previously closed because data were unavailable. How satellites are used to collect information useful to weather forecasters and research meteorologists and how these measurements made from outside the atmosphere can be used to supplement conventional observations made within the atmosphere will be described in this book. We will also try to convey an understanding of the many problems facing the meteorologist as a scientist and as a weather forecaster and how satellite data can be used to help solve them.

The basic function of the weatherman is to understand the earth's atmosphere. Much is known; much must be learned. It is known that the earth's atmosphere extends outward almost indefinitely, merging with the sun's atmosphere. Because the gases of the atmosphere are compressible, the earth's gravitational force packs half of the mass of the atmosphere into the lowest 3½ miles; at 10 miles above the earth, 90 per cent of the atmosphere is left below. Almost all the weather that directly affects man's activities occurs in the troposphere—the lowest 5 to 6 miles of the atmosphere. In this incredibly thin skin of air, tons of rain, snow, sleet, hail, and drizzle are produced and deposited on the earth's surface every day; 2,000 thunderstorms crackle every hour; winds range from gentle zephyrs to raging hurricanes and tornadic furies that can play tiddlywinks with a thirty-ton reinforced-concrete roof; and temperatures range from those that have preserved glaciers for millions of years to record highs of over 130° Fahrenheit.

This potpourri of extremes falls into a coherent system when the atmosphere is considered as a whole; it is chaos that defies understanding when only a small segment is known. Knowledge of the whole is the essence of the meteorological problem. It is here that the weather satellites are contributing essential information never before available.

In principle, every cubic mile of air is coupled to every other cubic mile of atmosphere through bonds of motion, acceleration, and pressure. Kinetic energy created by an intensifying storm over the mid-Pacific can affect weather in the United States long before the winds from that storm have reached the west coast of the continent. This is the broad scale aspect of atmospheric motion. Small-scale disturbances are superimposed on, affect, and are affected by the larger scale motions.

The atmosphere can be compared to a huge steam engine; the atmosphere is the "steam" and the sun is the fire that heats the "boiler." The earth and its atmosphere are heated unevenly by the sun. The equatorial regions receive more solar heat over every square mile of surface than do the polar regions. This differential heating is the primary cause of atmosphere circulation. The heated air of the tropics expands and rises; as it moves up and away, cooler, heavier air from the north and south moves in to replace it.

Differential heating by the sun alone would lead to north and south winds only, but the main wind belts are east or west winds. The earth's rotation provides the necessary deflective force for these. An explanation of this effect of the earth's rotation on the direction of

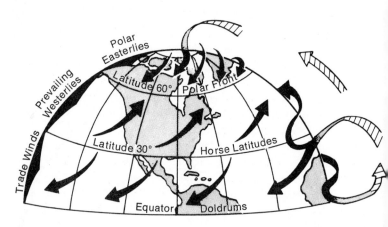

Figure 1.1 General circulation of the atmosphere in three wind belts.

wind flow can be found in almost any introductory text on meteorology or oceanography under the heading "Coriolis force." It is sufficient here to know that the Coriolis force causes wind and water currents to curve to the right in the northern hemisphere and to the left in the southern hemisphere.

The effects of differential heating and the earth's rotation are further complicated by friction between the atmosphere and the earth. The combined interactions produce three main zonal wind belts in each hemisphere; the tropical easterlies, the mid-latitude westerlies, and the polar easterlies, shown schematically in Figure 1.1. Storms and other disturbances are born, pass through their life cycles, and die as they are carried along in these general wind belts. Frequently they move from one wind belt to another during their lifetimes. An example is the hurricane; it is born in equatorial latitudes, drifts westward in the tropical easterlies, and very often curves poleward and is then carried back toward the east in the mid-latitude westerlies. When and where will such a storm be born? How will it grow and move? This is the forecast problem.

A wind belt can be considered a complete band of winds girdling a hemisphere. Although air motion in mid-latitude westerlies is predominantly from west to east, it meanders to form a wavelike pattern.

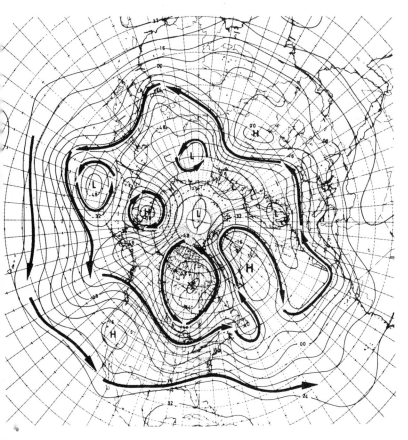

Figure 1.2 A typical 500-mb chart for winter over the Northern Hemisphere. The contours represent heights of the 500-mb surface with 200 feet (60 meters) between contours. The heavy arrows represent wind flow.

Figure 1.2 is a map of the Northern Hemisphere diagramming in a schematic fashion the main west wind belt. These patterns represent the average flow of air in the troposphere, where more than half of the atmosphere is found. The patterns formed as the westerly wind belt is deflected first northward then southward are waves quite analogous to those on a water surface. The familiar water waves are disturbances which produce oscillations in the water height, that is, disturbances in the vertical. Although waves in the wind belts have extremely small vertical components, they have appreciable side-to-side wave motion in the horizontal plane,* as shown in Figure 1.1. These atmospheric waves in the zonal wind belts are quite similar to waves in other fluids and so can be treated by using the same mathematical theory used to treat other fluid phenomena. Thus, atmospheric motion can be studied by application of hydrodynamic theory, the theory of continuous fluid substance in motion.

Low pressure areas, sites suitable for the formation of new storms or for the intensification of existing ones, are induced where the westerlies dip southward in the wave troughs. An intensifying wave trough makes its effect felt in the next trough downstream (perhaps 3,000 miles to the east), because both are part of the same wave train. Thus, every forecast for periods in excess of 24 hours must be based upon a knowledge of the entire wave pattern as well as myriad other details. The forecaster, whether an experienced meteorologist or an electronic computer operating on hydrodynamical equations, can produce an intelligent forecast only when the complete state of the atmosphere is known at the beginning of the forecast period.

No storm is an independent entity—its entire life cycle is controlled by the long wave pattern. Determining the larger scale wave pattern is an objective way of bringing sound dynamic theory to bear on the questions of "Where is potential energy available to produce a storm?" and "What effect will release of that energy have on the carrying wind current itself?"

---

* Strictly speaking, the waves are not in a "plane" but on the spherical surface of the earth. Because they have very long wavelengths, this spherical shape must be incorporated into the mathematical formulations used in dealing with them.

It is beyond the scope of this book to discuss the methods of forecasting the large-scale circulation, but it is pertinent to consider the
form and nature of energy storage in the atmosphere. Detection and
measurement of this energy is the purpose of weather observations.
It has already been pointed out that the basic energy source is the
sun. Heating produces stores of energy in the atmosphere in two
forms. First, an enormous amount of energy goes into evaporating
water from the oceans. Wherever this water vapor is condensed, the
same amount of energy is released; so the moist air currents are
the storehouse of tremendous amounts of latent energy, awaiting the
proper circumstances for release. Second, as heated air expands and
rises, every gram of air thus raised has potential energy that will be
converted into kinetic energy when the air sinks. It is this effect that
creates the atmospheric pressure differences that produce the winds,
which in turn transport moist air to the site of a generating hurricane
or blizzard.

Viewed on this scale, it becomes evident that the meteorologist
must have weather observations of all kinds, in adequate numbers
over large areas, to describe the location of the wave troughs and
the motions of stores of latent and potential energy. Great skill and
worldwide facilities are required to assemble these data into one
coherent picture. This is done every day, at least twice a day, and
this observation and analysis operation must precede every forecast.

Now how well is this "complete state of the atmosphere" observed
with the conventional network of weather stations? In spite of highly
organized weather services, and the tremendous development of
meteorology as a science over the past hundred years, the weather
forecaster has always been handicapped by lack of sufficient data.
Even today, with rapid communication, highly developed instruments
to measure parameters important to weather forecasting, and worldwide cooperation through the World Meteorological Organization,
there are still vast areas of the globe from which routine weather
observations are not available. The oceans, covering seven-tenths of
the earth, and the arctic wastes, deserts, high mountains, and jungles
are areas of inadequate observations. Even in areas with dense
observational networks, such as Europe and the United States, the

Figure 1.3 Map of the Northern Hemisphere showing locations of upper air observation stations.

average distance between surface stations is more than 90 miles, and between upper air observing stations it is more than 200 miles. The map shown in Figure 1.3 indicates approximately the areas of the earth from which weather observations are routinely available each day. Each dot represents an upper air observation station. Note the density of stations over Europe and the United States and the scarcity of stations over the oceans. The continents of the Northern Hemisphere are the only areas where there are relatively adequate observing networks. This map shows graphically that more of the atmosphere is unobserved than is observed. The forecaster today must operate on the basis of judicious estimates and extrapolation of weather parameters between widely spaced observations. An observing technique that could fill these vast voids has been the dream of meteorologists since routine weather services have been in existence.

The history of observation dates back to primitive man. The date of the invention of wind vanes, which show wind direction, is lost in antiquity. Scientific weather observations began with the invention of two basic instruments: the thermometer by Galileo in 1593, and the barometer by Torricelli about 1643. The barometer was initially used to show differences in elevation. Day-to-day fluctuations in the height of the mercury were noted when the barometer was not in use. Almost 200 years passed after the invention of these two basic instruments before such people as Admiral Fitzroy and Edmund Halley mapped the movement of weather systems and wind fields.

Observations of clouds furnished the first clues to the three-dimensional structure of the atmosphere. In 1803, Luke Howard classified clouds as cirrus, cumulus, and stratus. These three simple classifications named the feathery ice crystal clouds of the high atmosphere (cirrus), the clouds of vertical development (cumulus), and the layered structure of some cloud forms (stratus). By closer observation, Howard defined intermediate forms, such as cirrocumulus and cirrostratus. Later observers developed the classification system in use today which separates ice crystal clouds from those formed of water droplets, classifying clouds according to the heights at which they occur, their structure, and the physical processes involved in their formations.

Meteorologists of the late 19th and early 20th centuries realized that typical cloud patterns could be associated with various broad scale atmospheric patterns. The appearance of certain types of clouds was connected with the movement of pressure patterns, temperature changes, and wind flow. It was noted that clouds at certain levels in the sky often moved in directions different from clouds below or above them, that some clouds grew vertically, and that others appeared to remain at the same level. All these observations led to the development of the cyclone and frontal theories of the Norwegian school of meteorologists. These theories could have come into being only upon recognition of the fact that there are vertical as well as horizontal motions in the atmosphere.

As soon as the three-dimensional structure of weather patterns was accepted as fact, attempts were made to obtain measurements of winds and temperatures in the layers of air above the ground. In 1895, Professor Marvin attached instruments to kites to obtain temperatures at various heights above the ground. Later, in 1909, balloons filled with hydrogen were released and their flight paths noted in order to compute the directions and speeds of the winds high above the ground. Ten years later, in 1919, instruments were attached to the wings of airplanes to measure the temperature, pressure, and humidity of the atmosphere at flight levels. The airplane also gave weathermen their first chance to see clouds from above. Radiosondes, lightweight instruments which measure temperature, humidity, and pressure as they are carried aloft by free balloons and transmit the measurements to the ground by radio, were first used routinely in 1936. Shortly after radar was developed it was used to track balloons carrying metallic targets. This is the RAWIN (radar wind) system which is now used to observe the winds above the ground. Wind measurements at heights as high as 100,000 feet are routinely collected by this radar wind system. Radar that can be used to detect precipitation is also used to track thunderstorms, hurricanes, or any clouds from which rain or other precipitation is falling.

During World War II, great advances were made in communications and rocketry. The war benefited meteorology through the invention of radar, improvements in other communications techniques, the greatly expanded network of radiosonde stations (in support of aviation), and the development of rockets. The German V–2 rockets, brought to the United States after the war, gave scientists the opportunity to measure various atmospheric parameters at heights far beyond the reach of the radiosonde balloons.

When photographs obtained from rockets were examined, it was found that the configurations of cloud patterns reflected the motion of the air that carried them. Even before high altitude photographs were available, the great value of a large-scale cloud cover "map" was discussed, because clouds are good evidence of available water vapor. When rocket and television technology advanced to the stage where an orbiting television system appeared possible, the idea excited considerable interest. Feasibility studies conducted in the early 1950's culminated in the design of the TIROS satellite.

TIROS (the *T*elevision and *I*nfra*R*ed *O*bservation *S*atellite), with its television cameras and infrared radiometers, opened the era of global weather observations, with its routine gathering of information previously unavailable. When TIROS commenced operating in April, 1960, the meteorologist had added to his array of observing instruments a new and powerful tool. Newspapers brought the story of this new program to their readers with great enthusiasm but, unfortunately, with some inaccuracies. The meteorological satellite was sometimes hailed as a "forecasting satellite," and even today the term is slipped into print by a reporter who is unaware of the distinction between observation and analysis and the forecasting based on analysis. The weather satellite is an observing tool and, in the foreseeable future, will be used only for observation. TIROS emerged as a result of man's long effort to observe the atmosphere.

2

• • • •

Observing from Space

As a platform for observation, the artificial satellite so far transcends balloons, aircraft, and rockets that at last man can now hope to achieve an adequate sampling of the atmosphere. However, the data obtained are quite different in nature from those gathered by most earth-bound instruments, or by sensors carried on balloons or aircraft. The more conventional instruments are immersed in the fluid they measure, while satellites carry their sensors far outside the atmosphere.*

* It is true that some extremely tenuous atmosphere exists at satellite altitudes but we are concerned here with the atmospheric layers of the troposphere and the lower stratosphere.

Let us consider the measurement of atmospheric temperature. An international network of upper air stations obtains air temperatures at various levels in the atmosphere by using a thermometer attached to a free-floating balloon. The temperature readings are sent to the ground by radio. By contrast, a thermometer aboard a satellite some hundreds of miles above the weather-bearing atmosphere can yield no such information. Satellite instruments obtain data only by sensing electromagnetic radiation from the earth and its atmosphere. Visible light is a form of electromagnetic radiation, as are infrared radiation, microwaves, and radio waves. Radiation of this type is *the only link between the satellite and the atmosphere*. Furthermore, the instruments are carried on a vehicle that must move according to the laws of celestial mechanics; hence, it is in a fixed path and cannot be maneuvered like an aircraft. This fact has both advantages and disadvantages. Fortunately the advantages are tremendous, while the difficulties can be minimized.

Satellites bring two distinct benefits to meteorology. The first is the tremendous increase in the frequency and area of observation provided. By choosing the orbit properly, it is possible for a single satellite to "look" at each point on earth twice every 24 hours, or alternately, to keep a significant portion of the earth's surface under continual watch every minute of the day. The second advantage results from having the instruments outside the atmosphere. Only from such a vantage point can the heat budget of the planet be assessed. Instruments can measure the total energy reflected and radiated into space by the earth and its atmosphere. Simultaneously, other instruments can measure the total amount of energy arriving from the sun at the "top of the atmosphere." The difference between these is the amount absorbed by the atmosphere and oceans. It is this captured energy that is the fuel for the heat engine that produces our weather. The use of radiation measurements is discussed in Chapters 5 and 6; here we will only outline the principal characteristics of electromagnetic radiation and mention how knowledge of these characteristics can be used.

Electromagnetic radiation is energy transmitted in wave form. The familiar wave energy of water is essentially two-dimensional, but electromagnetic waves radiate in all directions from their source without the need for a conducting medium. This radiation proceeds with minimum loss through a vacuum at the speed of light, about 186,000 miles per second (3×10^{10} cm/sec). Ultraviolet rays, visible light, infrared (heat) waves, and radio waves are all radiation of this type. Each of these names applies to a general group of frequencies which span a large range. The middle frequency of visible light waves is about 6×10^{14} cycles per second. The frequency of radio waves in the broadcast band is typically 1×10^{6} cycles per second— 600 million times lower.

Just as one can measure the wavelength (the distance from one wave crest to the next) in water waves, the wavelength of electromagnetic waves can also be computed. The wavelength of the higher frequencies is referred to in terms of a length unit called the "micron," which is one-millionth of a meter. Visible light waves at a frequency of 6×10^{14} cycles per second have a wavelength of 0.5 microns. For the lower frequencies it is more convenient to use length units of meters, centimeters, or millimeters. The radio waves of 10^{6} cycles per second have a wavelength of 300 meters. The wavelength of radar waves is typically about 5 centimeters.

The significance of this broad range of wavelengths is that different wavelengths interact with matter in very different ways. Due to its molecular structure, a given substance may be highly permeable to one group of wavelengths but completely opaque to others. Every reader is familiar with examples of this fact. For instance, a radio works equally well inside a windowless room or exposed to the sky. The longer wavelengths of the radio waves penetrate the walls of the room which are, in turn, opaque to the shorter wavelengths of light. Between the extremes of permeability and opacity are all degrees of translucency. Deriving meteorological information by measuring radiation is the science of exploiting these differences.

What wavelengths are radiated from earth, what wavelengths do we receive from the sun, and how can we derive meteorological information from radiation? The sun radiates throughout a very wide spectrum, from waves shorter than visible light (ultraviolet) to the very long infrared and even some radio waves. Just like every other

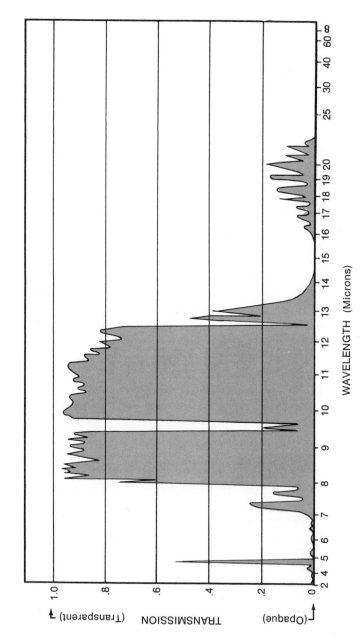

Figure 2.1 Transmission characteristics of the earth's atmosphere.

radiating body, the sun emits *most* of its energy at a relatively small group of wavelengths; its wavelength of maximum emission is determined by its temperature. The hotter a radiating surface, the shorter the wavelength at which it emits its maximum energy and the greater the total intensity of radiation. The sun, with an effective radiating temperature of nearly 5800°K,* radiates most of its energy as visible light. Approximately 50 per cent of the sun's energy is emitted in the wavelengths between 0.3 and 0.8 microns.

The earth-atmosphere radiating temperature is about 250°K, so our planet radiates no visible light. Instead, its maximum radiation is in the infrared wavelengths, with 50 per cent of the energy radiated in the interval of 6 to 16 microns. The hot sun emits radiation at a rate 100,000 times greater than the cool earth.

Most of the sun's energy used by our atmospheric heat engine is first absorbed by the ocean and land areas. Some is used immediately in evaporating water from the earth's surface, but only a small part is absorbed directly by the atmosphere, which is quite transparent to visible light. However, vegetation, soil, rocks, and water all absorb energy of solar wavelengths. The warmed surface then radiates long infrared waves skyward. Since the atmosphere is nearly opaque to some of these longer waves, it absorbs them and is heated. Since the atmosphere is not uniformly opaque to all infrared wavelengths, measurement of radiation in various small wavelength intervals reveals different details about the atmosphere.

Although dry atmosphere is some 99 per cent oxygen and nitrogen, the relatively small amount of water vapor and carbon dioxide in the remaining 1 per cent accounts for most of the absorption of infrared radiation. Despite this property, these latter gases are transparent to emission in specific groups of wavelengths. Figure 2.1 depicts the essential details of the non-uniform absorption. For example, water vapor is nearly transparent to radiation in wavelengths from about 8 to 12 microns. So this range is called the "water vapor window."

---

* Temperatures in radiation work are usually expressed in the Kelvin scale, written "°K." Zero degrees Kelvin is equivalent to −273.16° Centigrade; 5800°K is equal to 5526.84° Centigrade.

• • • • • • •

Radiation from the earth's surface easily penetrates the atmosphere in this "window" and thus can be measured by a satellite-borne instrument sensitive to this particular group of waves. Since the intensity of this radiation is controlled by the temperature of the surface that emits the waves, measurements of radiation flux in the 8 to 12 micron band can be converted to surface temperatures. But this radiation from the surface cannot penetrate clouds, so the satellite instrument does not always "see" the earth's surface. In areas where the surface of the earth is cloud-covered, it is the radiation from the top of the clouds that reaches the satellite instrument. In this case the radiation measurement can be used to compute the cloud-top temperature. Since the temperature of the atmosphere generally decreases with increasing altitude at a known rate, an estimate of cloud-top altitude can be made from the computed temperature of the cloud top. In areas where no clouds exist, the warmer temperatures derived from satellite measurements represent earth or ocean surface temperatures. Both of these pieces of information are valuable meteorological data.

More than 99 per cent of the earth's radiation is emitted in the infrared wavelengths which range from 3 microns to about 40 microns. Radiation in this range thus represents the total loss to space of the energy previously absorbed from the sun. Satellite sensors which are capable of making measurements in this wavelength interval provide the data needed to study the energy budget of our planet; some aspects of this investigation will be discussed in later chapters. Some of the visible light from the sun which reaches the atmosphere and the surface of the earth is reflected and scattered back to space without being absorbed. This is the energy sensed by the satellite television cameras to produce the pictures of cloud cover. The intricacies of exploiting these data will also be discussed later.

There are three types of problems in designing and using the new observing platform. They involve sensing, engineering, and interpretation or analysis of the data. All these problem areas interact with each other more intimately in the space program than in the older weather observing systems. The *problems of sensing* arise because the atmospheric physicist must devise techniques to use the emitting, scattering, and reflecting characteristics of the planet and its atmosphere to obtain useful information from satellite altitudes. The *engineering and design problems* result from the requirements for rugged, lightweight, and low power-consuming instruments with which to measure specified portions of the radiation spectrum. Sending the information from the satellite to the earth creates additional engineering problems. *Analysis problems* face the meteorologist because he must learn to use these data, which are so different from those he previously worked with.

The solutions of these problems cannot be obtained independently in each area, because every solution in one area affects the other areas. Some compromise is always required between cost and the state of technology. To gain an advantage in one area, something may have to be sacrificed in the others; in engineering jargon, these are "trade-offs."

To illustrate this point, let us consider the following. A broad field of view in each television picture is essential if maximum meteorological use is to be made of these data. At the same time, good picture resolution* is desirable if important features, such as boiling thunderstorm clouds, are to be distinguished from passive, high altitude ice clouds. It is easily within the present "state-of-the-art" to satisfy both requirements, but at what expense? Cloud pictures are transmitted to earth by scanning the television camera tube with a series of lines. The TIROS one-half inch cameras employ about 500 lines per picture; the TOS (*T*IROS *O*perational *S*atellite) one-inch vidicons use 800 lines. If greater resolution is required, more lines must be used. Later in this chapter this problem will be discussed in more detail, but it is sufficient here to note that to produce more lines requires a larger television tube and more power to operate it.

Even if the extra weight and the larger power supply and auxiliary equipment could be included in the budget for a given program (and this additional weight might be the "last straw" for the rocket, so that a larger and more expensive booster would be needed), the

---

* The term "resolution" in photography is used to express the resolving ability of a system, that is, the ability to reveal that two closely spaced elements are indeed two, and not a single image.

engineer faces a more severe problem: that of transmitting this additional information to earth. Television pictures as well as other data from the satellite are sent to earth by frequency-modulated (FM) radio which requires the transmitter to be within line-of-sight of the receiving station. Unless a relay communication satellite is used, the ground station can receive data only while the vehicle is above the horizon, so rapid read-out of stored data is essential. A feature of frequency-modulated transmission is that a whole group of frequencies must be transmitted simultaneously. The total frequency interval is known as the *bandwidth* of that particular signal. A basic characteristic is that more information can be transmitted per second by increasing the bandwidth; conversely, the same total amount of information can be transmitted over a smaller bandwidth if a longer transmission time is used. With television pictures, the total amount of information to be sent is proportional to the number of scan lines. Thus, more information in the form of greater picture detail must be secured at the expense of greater bandwidth or more transmission time. Greater bandwidth requires greater power—a heavier power supply system.

For a given orbit the time for signal transmission cannot be increased; the satellite races across the sky at a rate determined by celestial mechanics. not by the demands of communications engineers. The obvious solution is therefore to increase bandwidth (and power and weight). Increasing the spacecraft weight could be a serious obstacle but the availability of bandwidth may turn out to be more serious. The tremendous expansion of radio communication requires careful coordination between projects to avoid interference; so this last problem is by no means a minor one.

What alternatives are open? Bandwidth and time might be reduced by transmitting less information; less information can be translated into fewer pictures or fewer lines per picture. The engineers and meteorologists must decide on just what trade-off to make. Clearly cost, size, and communication on the one hand must be balanced against degradation of the data on the other. The television system used on meteorological satellites has not been designed to the limit of technology because it has been necessary to accept some trade-off.

Such compromises have a profound effect on interpretation of the data. If we return to the example of the thunderstorm clouds, poor resolution makes it impossible to recognize an individual cloud of this type by its characteristic cauliflower appearance. This has made it necessary to search for a more indirect means of identifying thunderstorms. An investigation in which satellite pictures were correlated with ground observed thunderstorms showed that the presence of thunderstorms can frequently be deduced from the pattern and appearance of thunderstorm cloud groups. The organization of the satellite cloud pattern in which thunderstorms were found to exist was on a scale not known or observed before. But research had to be completed before these satellite data could be so interpreted. This example illustrates the interaction between the design and analysis of the data. The interpretation problem would not have existed were it not for the necessary engineering-design compromises.

Observing from a spacecraft in orbit is quite different than observing from any other vehicle, because the laws of celestial mechanics must be taken into account. No amount of technological advance can change the physics of bodies in orbit; so orbital effects will always influence the design of meteorological satellites. The relation of the orbital period to the satellite track across the earth's surface and the relation between the sun and the satellite orbit are determined by celestial mechanics.

There is an immutable relationship between satellite height and the time it takes the satellite to make a circuit of the earth. The graph of Figure 2.2 shows how the satellite *period* (time for one circuit) increases with increasing height. While the satellite circles the earth in a plane whose orientation in space is nearly stationary, the earth rotates inside the satellite orbit at a rate of one revolution every 24 hours, or 15° of longitude in one hour. Thus, a satellite whose period is two hours will cross the equator 30° of longitude further west on each successive orbit.* This, in turn, requires that

---

* This applies to satellite orbits that are inclined to the equatorial plane. A satellite in an orbit that coincides with the equatorial plane would never move north or south of the equator, and at every longitude the equator would be directly beneath the satellite.

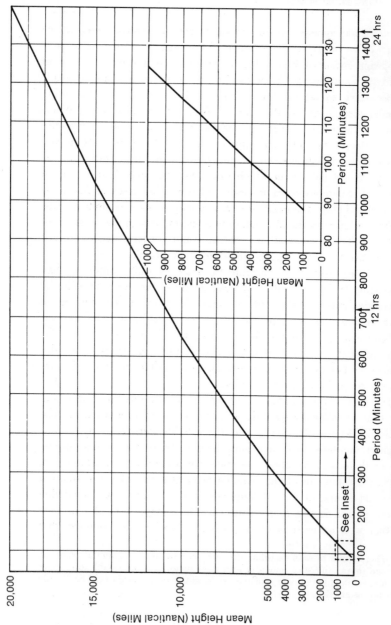

Figure 2.2 Graph of satellite period (labeled in minutes along the bottom) versus satellite mean altitude (labeled in nautical miles along the left).

the satellite instruments must have a field of view wide enough to span 30° of longitude (a distance of 1,800 nautical miles) in order to "see" every point on earth during a 24-hour period. A smaller field of view would leave gaps between adjacent equator traverses.

The distance between successive passes would be less if the satellite were lower (and thus moving faster), but a vehicle at very low altitudes would be short-lived. Atmospheric drag would cause the satellite to drop lower and lower, and finally burn up in the dense atmosphere. A satellite orbiting at heights somewhat above 100 miles would probably outlast the electronic equipment it carried, but observations at the edges of the field of view would be made at such large oblique angles that they would be of little value. The data obtained by a sensor viewing an area at a large oblique angle is seriously degraded; this characteristic is one of the important parameters affecting the design of instruments and the choice of an orbit. The requirement for uniformly good data over the entire globe makes these considerations critical to the meteorological satellite system. The problems are illustrated by considering television picture images of the earth from a satellite.

In effect, each television picture is composed of a network of "spots," each with a different shade of gray. The TIROS pictures, for example, were transferred to film by 500 scan lines. Each scan line has the ability to portray about 500 *changes* of light intensity along its length. The picture is thus a matrix of 500 by 500 spots. Two small features that lay within one spot on the camera tube would not be reproduced on film as two features; both would contribute to a single light intensity that would determine the shade of gray of that single spot. The spot size is thus a measure of the resolution of the system. Each spot subtends a small but finite angle, as illustrated in Figure 2.3. In this sketch one such spot *a* on the focal plane of the camera is bounded by rays forming the solid angle *a*. Extended to the earth's surface this spot *a* represents the area *A* on earth. The size of spot *a* and the size of the angle *a* are determined by the design of the camera and so are fixed for a given system. But the size of the area *A* depends upon other things as well. It is the size of this "spot" on earth that is important because no detail smaller

• • • • • • •

than A can be recorded. The schematic configuration of Figure 2.3 shows the same angle a intersecting the earth immediately beneath the satellite in area A_1 and about two-thirds of the way out toward the horizon in area A_2. Both the oblique view and the curvature of the earth's surface contribute to making A_2 very much larger than A_1. In the region of the picture at A_2 the resolution is much poorer than at A_1, thereby causing loss of detail and making interpretation more difficult.

It is easy to see that the more oblique the angle is to the edge of the field of view, the poorer the picture resolution will be. Thus, if a satellite were put into a low orbit in an attempt to attain a small distance between successive equator crossings, the resolution in the equatorial area midway between passes would be poor because of the large oblique viewing angles. Therefore, a low orbit is not suitable for a satellite that must view each spot on earth every day. An excessively high spacecraft is also unsuitable because it circles the earth so slowly that large distances between successive passes again cause the angle of view to the midpoint between passes to be unfavorable. The best compromise between these opposing effects can be attained by choosing an orbit of about 1,000 miles. At this altitude the oblique angle to the midpoint between passes is minimized.

In addition to causing decreased resolution, oblique views have yet another disadvantage, which is illustrated in Figure 2.4. Although the true fraction of the sky covered by clouds is about one-half in this sketch, the picture would show varying amounts of coverage at different viewing angles. Three angles from cloud to satellite are shown. If the camera were directly overhead, the tilt angle* would be zero and the true proportion of cloudy to clear area would be pictured. If the satellite were $30°$ from overhead, the cloudy area would appear larger than it actually is. In this particular example a view $45°$ from the vertical would show the whole field of view filled with clouds. The picture would appear to show an overcast area, while the true coverage is only 50 per cent. Of course, the angle at which the clear spaces between the clouds disappear in the picture

---

* Also referred to as the satellite *zenith* angle.

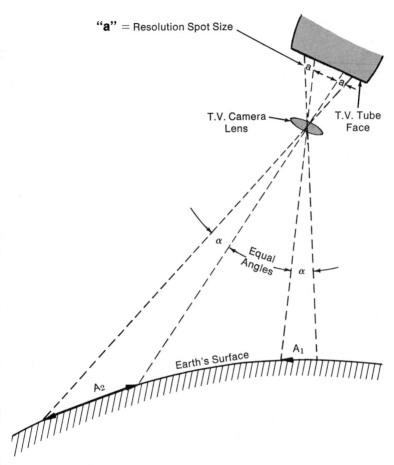

Figure 2.3 Schematic sketch of the relation between the resolution "spot" size, *a*, on the television tube face and the corresponding photographed areas of the earth's surface, A_1 and A_2.

depends upon the vertical extent and areal distribution of the clouds as well as the actual fraction of cloud cover.

The same geometric considerations apply to radiation measurements. Infrared sensors usually scan and record a single spot at one time, but in the data processing each spot is positioned in the appropriate place to make an infrared "picture." The spots that are sensed at large oblique angles are larger than those beneath the satellite and have correspondingly less resolution.

Let us suppose that radiation from the cloud field of Figure 2.4 were being recorded by the scanning spot of an infrared sensor sensitive to wavelengths in the water vapor window. At 0° tilt angle the clear spaces between the clouds would radiate at a high intensity, corresponding to the warm surface, while the cloud areas would radiate at their colder cloud-top temperatures. When these data were mapped they would appear as alternate areas of warm and cold temperatures corresponding to the broken cloud cover. At a tilt angle of 30° the warm area between the clouds would be so small that it would not be "resolved" by a single spot, but would contribute to the average radiating temperature sensed by the spot that encompasses some cloud top, some cloud side, and a small amount of surface. At a 45° viewing angle no warm surface would radiate to the satellite and radiation would be emitted entirely by cloud tops and sides. In this way the radiating temperature of the cloud field as measured at the satellite is greatly affected by the angle of view.

Finally, the position of the satellite orbit relative to the sun must be considered. Some observations require sunlight, while others require complete darkness. The best satellite track, from the point of view of maximum sunlight, should cross the daylight side of the earth at local noon and the night side at local midnight. A satellite launched into a polar orbit at local noon would produce this condition, but only for a short time.

The ideal situation would deteriorate to the worst possible condition in about three months, because the *orientation* of the plane of a polar orbit remains fixed in space, even though the plane is carried along with the earth in its orbit about the sun. For example, if the satellite were in a noon-midnight orientation on March 20, the great circle on the earth that divides the daylight from the night hemisphere (called the *terminator*) would be at right angles to the orbital

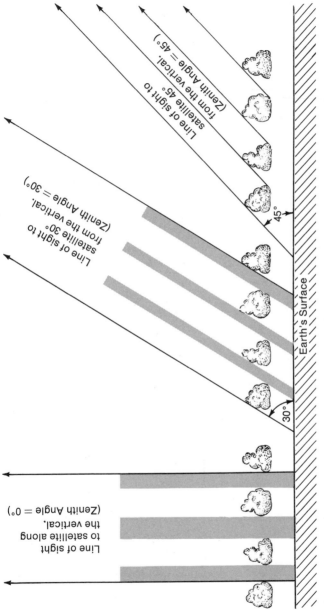

Figure 2.4 Cross section through fields-of-view for three different satellite positions. Shaded portions represent the cloud-free spaces that would be visible from the satellite.

• • • • • • •

plane. By June 20, the earth would have traveled approximately 90° in its orbit around the sun. But the orbital plane would not have rotated, so the terminator line and the orbital plane would be nearly* coincident and the satellite would circle the earth along the sunset-sunrise line. Gradually, during the next three months, the track would return to a favorable noon-midnight path, and then back to the twilight track three months later.

One solution to this problem is to launch vehicles into sun-synchronous orbits, that is, to attain an orbital plane that rotates about the earth at exactly the same rate as the earth orbits about the sun. Such motion would maintain the satellite track at a constant angle to the terminator line. An orbital plane will rotate in this manner if it is inclined so that the satellite moves from southeast to northwest. The angle of inclination required to obtain the correct rotation rate depends upon the satellite height. For a 750 nautical mile height, an inclination of about 80° is needed. The TOS and Nimbus spacecraft are put into such orbits.

So we see that the laws of celestial mechanics place certain restraints on a space vehicle carrying meteorological instruments. The scientist is not completely free to choose the time and place of observation or the angle of view for his instruments. Some further consideration of methods by which these difficulties are minimized is found in Chapter 7.

---

* The tilt of the earth's axis relative to the equatorial plane is neglected in this discussion.

3

• • • •

The First Five Years

of Weather Satellites

The spectacularly successful TIROS satellites were the culmination of more than ten years of studies and experiments to determine the feasibility of observing weather from space. The first picture experiment was carried on Vanguard II in February, 1959. Vanguard, one of the earliest of the United States satellites, was a gold-plated sphere 20 inches in diameter which weighed only $21\frac{1}{2}$ pounds. It had two telescopes pointed in opposite directions and mounted at 45° from the axis upon which the satellite was spinning. The sensing mechanism consisted of photoelectric cells mounted at the eyepiece, or

focus, of each telescope. Vanguard II circled the earth in an elliptical orbit once every 125.86 minutes, with perigee at 349 miles and apogee at 2,075 miles. As it traveled it spun on its axis at a rate of 50 revolutions per minute. The telescopes scanned across the earth as Vanguard spun. The varying intensities of sunlight reflected from clouds and from the earth's surface were measured by the photo-electric cells and recorded as electrical signals on magnetic tape in the satellite. These signals were radioed to the ground once during each orbit. A device had been designed to recompose the scan line signals into a crude photograph of the earth's cloud cover. Unfortunately, the vehicle wobbled on its spin axis, so the telescopes scanned the earth's surface in a criss-cross pattern. In addition, the orbit was far from circular, which added to the complications. As a result, it was not possible to obtain a picture from Vanguard II.

The same kind of television equipment was also unsuccessful on Pioneer I and II in October and November of 1958. Then, in August, 1959, a television system tried on Explorer VI sent some usable signals to earth. From these several pictures were constructed. While the quality of the pictures was poor, the success with this experiment encouraged further development which finally led to the TIROS television systems.

In the meantime, Professor Verner E. Suomi of the University of Wisconsin designed equipment which NASA (National Aeronautics and Space Administration) officials agreed to include on Explorer VII. The equipment, which would be used to measure the earth's radiation balance, consisted of black and white hemispheres, each mounted on a separate mirror and attached to the equator of the satellite (Figure 3.1). Mounting a hemisphere on a mirror has the same effect as exposing a complete sphere to radiation. The black sensor absorbs nearly all incident radiation; the white sphere absorbs only radiation with wavelengths longer than 4 microns, but reflects shorter wavelength radiation. The radiation measurements from Explorer VII were used to construct maps of temperature fields. These

Figure 3.1 (Opposite) Explorer VII satellite. The white and the black hemispheres mounted on the black rectangles are the Suomi radiometers. (Photo, courtesy of NASA.)

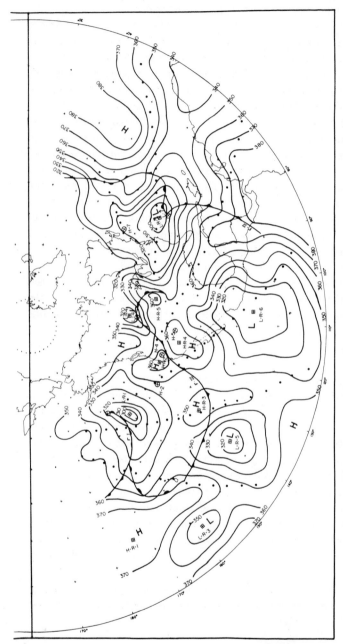

Figure 3.2 Long-wave radiation map from Suomi radiometer measurements. The contours are labeled in degrees Kelvin. Cold temperatures (areas marked *L*) represent cloudy areas; warm areas (marked *H*) represent clear skies. Fronts are time-adjusted to the radiation measurements. (Weinstein and Suomi, 1961.)

maps correspond quite well with the existing broad-scale cloud patterns of the weather maps (Figure 3.2).

In designing the TIROS satellite, full use was made of the experience gained in the experiments with earlier satellites. Those experiments established the feasibility of acquiring and storing radiation data in the satellite and transmitting these data to earth without serious loss of information. The technical problems of designing the instruments for weather satellites were many. One difficulty was miniaturization. For example, the vidicon tube used in the television system was reduced from the size used in earth-bound television cameras (about 18 inches long and 3 inches in diameter) to 3 inches long and $\frac{1}{2}$ inch in diameter. So it went with all the components; they were redesigned to reduce size and weight. Thus, it was possible to place in orbit a lightweight satellite capable of executing a number of complex functions upon radio command from earth.

The ultimate result of the TIROS design effort was a nearly cylindrical, eighteen-sided polyhedron, 22.5 inches high and 42 inches across, which was crammed with miniaturized components (Figure 3.3).

Since the first TIROS was launched, three types of weather satellites have been used: TIROS, Nimbus, and the "wheel" satellite. The last, a TIROS with special adaptations, is the basic spacecraft for the TIROS Operational Satellite (TOS) system. Nine TIROS of the original type were used. TIROS I was launched on April 1, 1960, and survived for 79 days. Operating time improved with successive satellites; by the end of 1965, TIROS VII and VIII had records of two and one-half and two years of successful operation. TIROS IX, the first of the wheel satellites, and Nimbus, a research and development vehicle, are described later in the chapter.

All TIROS satellites, both the original and the wheel types, are essentially alike in appearance and equipment. All carry two television cameras. A few carry radiometers to measure the solar and terrestrial radiation reflected from and emitted by the earth and its atmosphere. They are equipped with tape recorders, transmitters, and other electronic equipment to control the instruments and to transmit data from the cameras and the radiometers. There are also devices

on board the satellite to control its attitude and spin rate, and radio beacons whose signals are used by ground stations to follow the satellite in its orbit around the earth. All this equipment is built on the smallest possible scale to save space and reduce weight. Prior to launch, each piece is subjected to torturous tests, such as large temperature variations, vibration, shock, and exposure to near vacuum, to be sure it will survive the launch and perform reliably in orbit.

Each TIROS weighs about 300 pounds. The sides and top are covered with 9,620 solar cells to generate electricity from sunlight. This solar-generated electricity charges the batteries which are used to run all the electronic equipment on board.

Television cameras on weather satellites are quite different from those used in a broadcasting studio in that a satellite camera takes snapshots rather than "moving pictures." As in all cameras, there is an optical (lens) system and a shutter. At the focal plane, where an ordinary camera would have film, is the light-sensitive face of a special cathode ray tube called a *vidicon*. When the camera shutter is opened, an image is focussed on the tube face, and the various light intensities of the image form a pattern of electrical charges on the vidicon plate. These charges are retained on the tube face for many seconds without deterioration. An electron beam scans the tube face and converts the charges to a series of electrical signals, which can be transmitted immediately to a ground station or stored on tape for transmission on command from the ground. The electron beam scans across the picture horizontally, starting with a line at the top and completing the scan with a line across the bottom. After scanning, the tube is "wiped clean" electronically in preparation for the next picture.

Two basic types of camera vidicons have been used: the fast scan camera, which can either store the pictures on recording tape or send them directly to the special command and data acquisition stations; and the slow scan Automatic Picture Transmission (APT) camera.

Figure 3.3 (Opposite) TIROS IV spacecraft. Transmitting antenna is being fitted to baseplate. Note Suomi radiometers on rods extending out from baseplate. (Photo, courtesy of NASA.)

The fast scan camera used on the earlier TIROS has a ½-inch vidicon tube face. The scanning rate is 500 lines in 2 seconds. The vidicon currently in use has a 1-inch tube face. This larger tube, called the AVCS (Advanced Vidicon Camera System), has a scanning rate of 800 lines in 6.75 seconds. In effect, these lines of data consist of scan "spots" or discrete areas. The 500 line vidicon has 500 spots per line, and the 800 line vidicon, 800 spots per line. Thus the smaller picture consists of 250,000 data points, while the larger picture has 640,000 data points. Hence, the AVCS vidicon has a longer-scanning time.

The single purpose Automatic Picture Transmission camera broadcasts the signals generated by the scanning beam as the scanning is taking place. The 800 lines that constitute each APT picture are generated at a rate of 4 lines per second, so transmission of each picture takes 200 seconds. These signals can be received by relatively simple ground stations that can be installed almost anywhere, including truck-trailers and ships at sea. The pictures received by an APT station show the cloud cover over the station and the surrounding areas as it existed just about 3½ minutes earlier.

During the development of the operational weather satellite system, different fields of view were tried by using different lenses with the ½-inch vidicons. From the 400 mile heights at which they were used, the wide-angle cameras took a picture of a square area with sides approximately 800 miles long when the camera was pointed straight down. The field of view of the medium-angle camera was a square about 450 miles on a side, and that of the narrow-angle camera was about 80 miles on a side. The cameras used on the operational satellites of the TOS system have a square field of view 2,000 miles across, with pictures taken from a height of 750 nautical miles. The vidicon tube used with the AVCS and APT cameras of the TOS system satellites and with the Nimbus research and development satellite is the AVCS vidicon with a 1-inch face and 800 scan lines.

With a given vidicon, the resolution of picture elements can be changed by changing the "field-of-view." If a small field-of-view is focussed on a vidicon, it is scanned by the same number of lines as a large field-of-view, so smaller details are reproduced. Features as small as ½-mile across were visible in pictures taken by the early narrow-angle cameras from the 400-mile orbital height; the early wide-angle camera could resolve elements no smaller than 1.5 to 2 miles in diameter.

For general operational use, broad and continuous areas must be photographed. The narrow-angle pictures cannot cover a continuous area, so the large field-of-view wide-angle cameras must be used. On TIROS II the wide-angle camera, apparently damaged during launch, sent back only poor quality pictures. The TIROS II narrow-angle camera took pictures of excellent quality, some of which were used to study ice fields in the St. Lawrence estuary. But only parts of the important broad-scale cloud systems could be seen in the narrow-angle pictures. This experience with TIROS II led to the compromise plan of using either two wide-angle cameras or one wide-angle and one medium-angle camera on later TIROS satellites. So with reluctance, the decision was made to abandon the narrow-angle camera and to use only the lower resolution medium-angle and wide-angle cameras.

The initial series of TIROS satellites circled the earth once every 100 minutes at average heights of 450 statute miles. All were launched into nearly circular prograde (west to east) orbits.* The first four were placed in orbital planes inclined about 48° to the plane of the equator; TIROS V through VIII circuited the earth in orbits inclined 58° to the equatorial plane. Each was spin stabilized, spinning on its axis about 12 times per minute. This spinning motion, which acted as a gyroscope to prevent the satellite from tumbling, also kept it pointing toward the same point in space during each circuit of the earth. The cameras were mounted parallel to the spin axis, so these also pointed in one direction only. With this kind of stabilization, the cameras could take usable pictures during only 25 per cent of each orbit; during the remainder of the time they pointed either toward deep space or at angles so nearly tangent to the earth's surface that the pictures were of limited value. The initial attitude, determined by the manner in which the vehicle was launched, pointed the

---

* A prograde orbit is one in which the satellite travels in the direction of the earth's rotation.

Figure 3.4 TIROS orbiting earth. The cameras face the earth during daylight and space during darkness. (Photo, courtesy of NASA.)

cameras down toward earth during the daylight part of each orbit. When the satellite passed over the night side of the earth, its sensors pointed away from both the earth and sun (Figure 3.4). Most of the time the cameras viewed the earth at angles away from the vertical, so areas poleward of the satellite track on the earth could be photographed. TIROS satellites in the 58° orbit were able to take pictures of areas as far north and south as 70° of latitude.

TIROS, and now the TOS (TIROS Operational Satellite) wheel

spacecraft, are operated from ground stations at Wallops Island, Virginia, and Gilmore Creek (near Fairbanks), Alaska. All the equipment needed to send control messages to the satellite and to receive the data from the satellite is located at each of these command and data acquisition (CDA) stations. The operational procedure consists of two basic commands: one telling the satellite where to take pictures; the other directing it to send the pictures and other data to the ground receivers. Commands can be sent to the satellite directing it to carry out one, all, or any combination of the following actions:

(1) Remote mode photography. In this mode of operation the satellite is directed to take and store a series of pictures using either one or both of the cameras. These pictures are taken over areas out of telemetry range of the ground station and stored on tape recorders in the satellite.

(2) Direct mode photography. In this operation cloud photographs are taken while the satellite is within telemetry range of the station and transmitted immediately to the ground without on-board storage.

(3) Transmission command. When the satellite comes within range of a ground station it is commanded to send stored pictures and radiation data to the CDA station.

(4) Operations signals. Any electronic or attitude control system can be operated by appropriate signals from the ground stations.

The first eight TIROS in prograde orbits posed special problems, whereas control of the current TOS series of satellites is much simpler, as will be discussed later in this chapter. Before a command was sent to an early TIROS satellite, several things had to be considered. Most important was the knowledge of when the satellite would be in sunlight and when its cameras would be pointing toward the earth. This was not so simple as it may seem. These satellites, traveling at nearly 17,000 miles an hour, were nudged slightly out of the plane of their orbit each time they crossed the equator. This was caused by the slight differences in gravity between the equatorial bulge and the flattened polar regions. With the TIROS in a prograde orbit, the

• • • • • • •

effect of this nudging caused the orbital plane of the satellite to move slightly westward, or to *precess*, from day to day. This particular precession caused the orbital plane to rotate 360° relative to the "fixed" stars once every 75 days. One can visualize this precession by thinking of the orbit as a hoop attached to the earth's poles, but not touching the earth. As the earth spins eastward within the hoop, the hoop itself is very slowly turning in the opposite direction.

Precession of the orbit, plus the interaction of the magnetic field of the earth with that of the satellite, caused a daily change in the

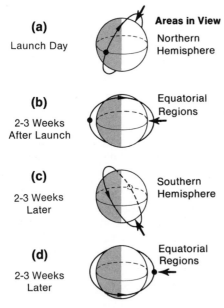

(a)
Launch Day

Areas in View

Northern
Hemisphere

(b)
2-3 Weeks
After Launch

Equatorial
Regions

Figure 3.5 Effect of precession of TIROS orbit on latitude in view.

(c)
2-3 Weeks
Later

Southern
Hemisphere

(d)
2-3 Weeks
Later

Equatorial
Regions

• Point where satellite crosses equator from south to north

➤ Direction in which cameras view

orientation of the satellite's spin axis, and hence, the direction in which its cameras pointed. The combined effects brought different latitudes into view. The day-to-day effect was small, but over a period of time the shift was so great that it was not always possible to take pictures where they were most needed. During a ten week cycle the viewing areas moved from the Northern Hemisphere to the Southern Hemisphere and back again (see Figure 3.5). Although magnetic coils on the early TIROS were somewhat useful in controlling attitude, full control was not possible. Adaptations of the magnetic coil system are now used for full control of the TOS spacecraft.

Once the areas of sunlight and the direction in which the camera could see (or camera attitude) were known, meteorologists of the National Weather Satellite Center decided which area was of greatest interest. Then the operation began. A signal was sent to the satellite as it passed over one of the ground stations. When the satellite reached the designated area, the clock system triggered the camera shutter. Once the camera started, it took a picture every 30 seconds until the magnetic tape storage capacity was reached. When the satellite again came within range, the ground station commanded it to transmit the stored data. If the station was in daylight and the cameras were pointed toward the ground, the satellite was commanded to take and transmit direct pictures. Finally, the clock was reset to take pictures during the next circuit of the satellite around the earth.

Until the middle of 1965, when a new system of centralized processing was started, the picture signals received from the satellite were simultaneously recorded on magnetic tape and displayed on a kinescope, a kind of television tube. The kinescope was photographed by an automatic 35 mm camera. Within minutes the film was developed, and the pictures were printed and given to the meteorologists for analysis of the pictured weather information. Details of this analysis, or reduction of the cloud pictures to a *nephanalysis* (cloud map), are given in Chapter 4.

The nephanalysis produced at the read-out station was then sent by facsimile to the Weather Bureau's National Weather Satellite Center at Suitland, Maryland. Here it was checked for consistency

and retransmitted by land line facsimile to weather stations all over the United States and by radio facsimile to the rest of the world. The analysis was also sent out as a coded message on international weather radio networks, so the information could be received by stations not equipped with radiofacsimile recorders.

With the present TIROS Operational Satellite system, the basic command operation of the satellite is much the same as under the earlier system, but the data processing has been centralized. The picture signals received at the Alaska and Virginia stations are immediately relayed without analysis to the data processing center at Suitland, Maryland. Here the signals are displayed on a kinescope and photographed in the usual manner. The cloud pictures either can be analyzed by the meteorologist or the signals can be fed immediately into a computer, which can produce a cloud-picture mosaic suitable for facsimile transmission directly to the users. If the data relay lines between the read-out stations and Suitland are temporarily out-of-order, then the data are analyzed at the read-out stations by the meteorologists. These hand analyzed data are then sent by telephone lines to the World Weather Center at Suitland for the usual relay to users all over the world.

The first eight TIROS satellites provided weather information never before available in any form. But there were two main problems: only about 20 per cent of the earth was visible to the satellite cameras on any one day; and not all latitudes could be photographed. The Nimbus satellite, with its earth-oriented sensors, was designed to correct these deficiencies. But before the first Nimbus could be launched, the wheel TIROS of the TOS system was designed and adopted as a less expensive alternate to the Nimbus satellite. However, because of its ability to carry a wide variety of experiments, the Nimbus satellite continues in use as a research and development vehicle. Future Nimbus satellites will carry improved instruments that must be tested before their incorporation into operational weather satellites. The first research and development (R&D) Nimbus was launched on August 28, 1964. It operated successfully until the

Figure 3.6   (Opposite) Nimbus weather satellite. (Photo, courtesy of NASA.)

mechanism that turned the solar paddles failed 27 days after launch. It carried three sensor systems: the advanced vidicon camera system (AVCS), an APT camera, and a high resolution infrared radiometer (HRIR).

The Nimbus satellite (Figure 3.6) is almost 11 feet high. Its base is a ring that contains the signal and control equipment and serves as a mount for the sensors. The main AVCS camera system consists of three vidicon cameras designed to function as a single unit. The central camera faces straight down to the earth; the flanking cameras are mounted at angles of 35° degrees to the center camera. Each "picture" taken as the three cameras are snapped simultaneously gives a view about 500 miles wide along the path of the satellite and 1,500 miles across this path. The pictures are stored on tape and subsequently transmitted to ground stations in exactly the same manner as the TIROS pictures are sent. Pictures are taken every 100 seconds. Each triad of pictures overlaps the previous set to provide a continuous strip of pictures from pole to pole.

The cameras and radiation sensors of a Nimbus satellite always face the earth as the satellite travels in a near-polar (80°) retrograde orbit. In this orbit a Nimbus travels from south-southeast to north-northwest on the side of the earth facing the sun. This is opposite to the way the first eight TIROS circled the earth. Although a retrograde orbit precesses, its precession is the reverse of that of the prograde orbits used earlier. The reverse precession causes the satellite to cross the equator at the same local time, orbit after orbit and day after day. Figure 3.7 compares the precession of a retrograde orbit with that of a prograde orbit. Earth-oriented cameras mounted on a satellite traveling in a retrograde orbit can take pictures of every part of the earth (except for the winter pole) once every 24 hours. The radiation sensors can take over on the dark side, so, in effect, a Nimbus satellite gives the weatherman a "look" at the entire earth twice every day.

The high resolution infrared (HRIR) sensors carried by Nimbus I measured ground and cloud-top radiation flux. The resolving power of the HRIR sensor is about 6 miles or roughly one-twelfth that of the AVCS cameras. The HRIR signals from Nimbus I were trans-

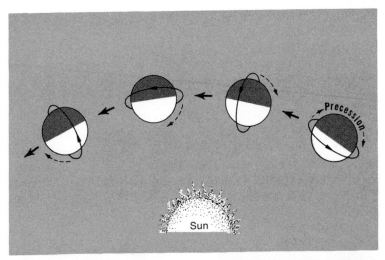

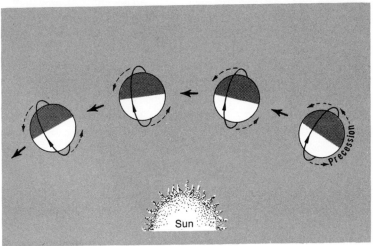

Figure 3.7 Precession of orbit plane as viewed from above the north pole. *(a)* Prograde orbit — westward precession. *(b)* Retrograde orbit — eastward precession. Satellite crosses the equator on the daylight side of the earth at the same local time every day if the orbit is sun-synchronous.

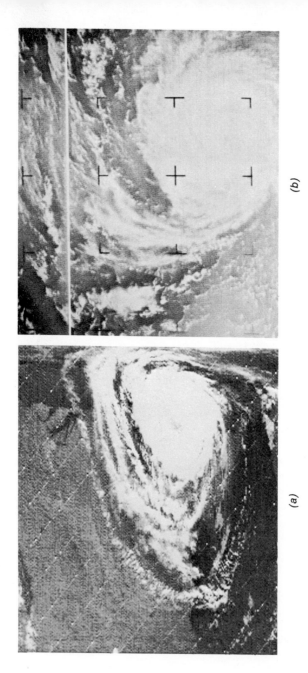

Figure 3.8 Hurricane Dora. (a) This picture shows high resolution infrared measurements made by Nimbus I. The measurements were made in darkness at 1:27 A.M., EDT, on September 9, 1964. (b) This photograph was taken a few days earlier than (a) in daylight by the APT camera of Nimbus. (Photo, courtesy of NASA.)

(a)

(b)

formed to excellent night pictures by converting them to various shades of gray, ranging from black to white (Figure 3.8). A strong signal received by the HRIR sensors represents a warm temperature, a weaker signal a colder temperature. By letting black represent a strong signal (warm temperature) and white the weakest signal (the coldest temperature), the HRIR signals were converted to pictures that look very much like cloud pictures taken in daylight. But note in Figure 3.8 how the pictures are "squeezed in" from the sides. This happened because no corrections were made for the distortions of the scan geometry. The temperature field represented by each shade of gray in the picture could be mapped on a standard map base. The cold areas would show the location of large cloud systems, while the warmer areas would depict ground or ocean surface. Temperature derived from the "bright" responses could also be used to determine the heights of the cloud tops. However, in making this determination a means would have to be found to distinguish between cold temperatures of snow and ice on the earth's surface and the equally cold temperatures of the tops of clouds some distance above the earth's surface. Very accurate climatological maps of surface temperatures would be helpful for differentiating snow and ice from cold clouds in using these HRIR pictures.

The APT camera, mentioned earlier, was first tested on TIROS VIII with indifferent success. But the APT test on Nimbus I was spectacularly successful. More than 50 stations scattered worldwide received clear, usable, and timely pictures as Nimbus passed overhead. The surprising aspect of the APT test was the amount of pictures a single APT station could receive in one day. The strip of pictures shown in Figure 3.9 was about 1,200 miles wide and more than 4,000 miles long. This strip was received at Washington, D.C., on August 29, 1964. The reception time for the strip was a few seconds over 16 minutes, and each picture in it was less than 4 minutes old when it was received.

The TIROS Operational Satellite system was designed to replace Nimbus as an operational satellite. TOS (Figure 3.10), a considerably less expensive satellite than Nimbus, is based on proven TIROS technology. Essentially, a TOS satellite is a TIROS tipped over on

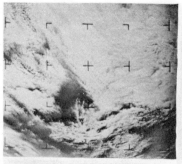
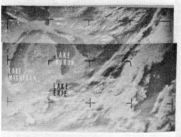
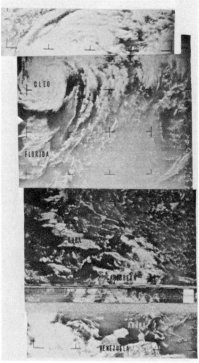

Figure 3.9 Nimbus APT photographs (picture strip 3,000 miles long) taken on August 29, 1964. Note hurricane Cleo over northern Florida, Georgia, the Carolinas, and Virginia. Blank areas and horizontally scrambled areas are due to radio interferences. (Photo, courtesy of NASA.)

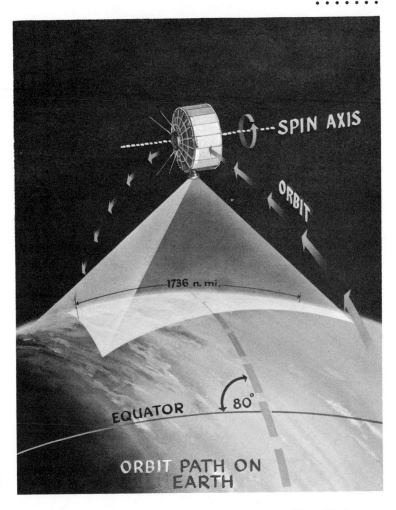

Figure 3.10 Diagram of TOS "wheel" satellite picture-taking attitude. (Photo, courtesy of ESSA.)

FIRST COMPLETE VIEW OF THE WORLD'S WEATHER

TIROS IX

FEBRUARY 13, 1965

SL1-65-6265

Figure 3.11 Global photomosaic of 450 pictures from TIROS IX, taken on February 13, 1965. (Photo, courtesy of ESSA.)

its side, with the cameras pointing out perpendicular to the spin axis instead of along the spin axis. This "cartwheel" satellite is spin-stabilized just as the early TIROS satellites were, but its spin axis is held perpendicular to the plane of the orbit. Thus, as TOS travels around the earth, it rolls along the orbit on its rim—hence, the name "cartwheel" or "wheel" satellite. Each camera points directly down toward the earth once each time the satellite rotates on its spin axis. In this way each picture is taken as the camera looks nearly straight down toward the earth's surface. With the TOS satellite in a near-polar sun-synchronous orbit, it is possible to obtain a picture of every part of the earth once every 24 hours. So this satellite is used in place of Nimbus because: (1) it has the same capability as Nimbus for photographing all the earth's surface, (2) it is designed to operate for at least a year—a much greater lifetime than Nimbus, and (3) it costs considerably less than Nimbus.

The TOS satellite concept was tested with TIROS IX, launched in January of 1965. TIROS IX went into a nearly sun-synchronous orbit, and its side-mounted cameras took pictures as this wheel satellite rolled along in its orbit. Pictures from this satellite gave weather-men their first global view of weather. Figure 3.11 is a global photo-mosaic of 450 pictures taken by TIROS IX on February 13, 1965. This spacecraft was also used to test the magnetic orientation coils designed to keep the spin axis perpendicular to the orbit and to maintain the spin rate of the satellite. Also tested were the horizon sensors used to trigger the cameras so that the pictures would be taken only when the lens was pointed straight down.

These tests were the final step toward making the TOS system a reality. TOS spacecraft, with their APT and AVCS cameras furnishing daily global cloud pictures, will be used until they can be replaced by satellites with performance and data collection capabilities superior to those now in use.

4

● ● ● ●

Data Acquisition

and Reduction

A weather satellite in orbit collects data in a routine, automatic fashion. These data, which are measurements made by the satellite's instruments, cannot be used until sent to the ground and processed. Since most of the measurements are made when the satellite is far from the ground stations, they must be converted into electrical impulses for storage in the satellite and for later transmission to the ground.

Data acquisition involves the transmission of the data from the satellite instruments and their reception by the earth-bound scientist.

• • • • • • •

Data reduction is the conversion of the signals which represent data into a form intelligible to the user. Thus, an important requirement is that the data be reduced to forms that can be used effectively, forms that might be quite different for different users. For example, the research meteorologist might be able to make most efficient use of the infrared intensity data if each piece of information were listed along with its geographical coordinates, so that each could be examined separately. But the busy forecaster could not use this information efficiently until it had been converted to effective temperatures and printed in map form by a computer. In this form it could be correlated with other meteorological information for timely operational use.

Data are sent from the satellite to the ground by radio signals. Once received at specially equipped ground stations, these data must be processed and transmitted to weather centers and forecast stations as quickly as possible. The first link in this communications network is the satellite-to-ground transmission. The satellite must be contacted by the ground station as it speeds around the earth. The FM radio transmission used also requires that the satellite be in a direct line-of-sight from the ground. Of course, it is impossible to see the satellite, so there must be a means of keeping tabs on its location at any instant. The satellite is equipped with a radio beacon, or "beeper." The beacon signals are received by a worldwide tracking network. By using these signals the exact location and the day-to-day orbit of the satellite can be calculated. An electronic computer is used to determine this orbit and also to predict future orbits. Other signals from the satellite "tell" the computer which way the cameras are pointing; from these the orientation of the satellite can be determined. With the orbit and orientation known or accurately predicted, it is possible to predict the exact time and number of minutes the satellite will be within direct line-of-sight of a ground station. A TIROS satellite in a 450 nautical mile orbit, for example, remains above the horizon of the station for 10 minutes if it passes within a 1,200 nautical mile radius of the ground antennae. The more nearly it comes to the center of the 1,200-mile radius circle around a station, the longer the ground station can retain contact. Each time the satellite passes within range, the ground station sends command signals to the "bird" and receives data.

The line-of-sight range from a station increases with the height of the satellite. For example, a satellite at an altitude of 810 statute miles would be within range of a station whenever it passed within 1,960 miles of it.

Pictures are readily usable and so are processed at once. The radiation data are more difficult to process and, at first, were used only for research. The pictures are used to make nephanalyses, or cloud maps. These "nephs," as the weatherman calls them, must be placed in the hands of users as soon as possible because weather information to be used for forecasting purposes quickly loses its usefulness. With few exceptions, information more than 24 hours old is useful mainly for research or long-range trend forecasting. After the nephanalyses are prepared, they are relayed by land line and radio to weather stations all over the world.

Most weathermen would like to be able to see the cloud pictures for themselves. But practical considerations come first. Each cloud map, made from 10 to 30 pictures, can be sent by facsimile in 20 minutes; each picture takes 8 minutes of transmission time. So it would take 4 to 12 times as long to send all of the pictures. If each station received the pictures, the meteorologists at the station would still have the problem of interpretation.

There are many problems connected with using the picture data. The most obvious one is to determine what meteorological information we can get from the picture. This is discussed in detail in Chapter 6. The others are optical and geometric—the photogrammetry problems. The optical problem stems from the fact that wide-angle lenses, with their resultant severe radial distortion and aberrations, have had to be used. A target of concentric circles and radial lines [Figure 4.1(a)] appears somewhat distorted when seen through the lens [Figure 4.1(b)]. To further complicate matters, each camera lens distorts the target image a little differently. In addition, electronic distortions of varying degrees of severity are introduced into the final image by minute imperfections in the vidicon face and in the electronic system itself. So before a satellite is sent into orbit, each

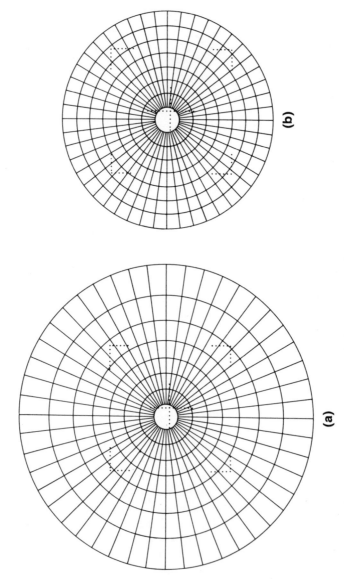

Figure 4.1 Vidicon test target and target photographed through vidicon lens. (*a*) Target seen with no distortions. (*b*) Target photograph showing the optical distortions which compress the dimensions of the outer portion of the field.

camera is tested. A detailed record of the optical and electronic distortions associated with each camera system is kept so the proper allowances for distortion can be made when the pictures from that camera are used. The details of the distortion are listed for use in rectifying and processing by computers.

The principal geometric problem with early TIROS pictures resulted from the fact that every television picture of the earth was taken from a slightly different angle. The size and shape of the photographed area is changed when the camera axis is tilted away from the vertical. The circular field-of-view of the lens intersects the earth's spherical surface in the form of a circle if the camera axis is directed

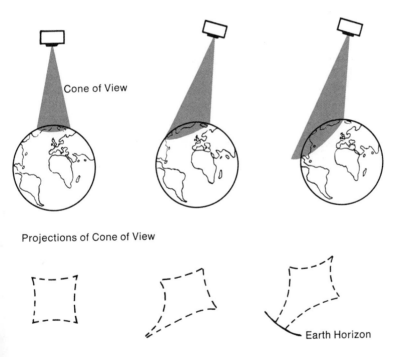

Figure 4.2 Actual shape of earth area in square satellite pictures taken from different angles.

straight down, and along a distorted egg-shaped curve if the axis is tilted. However, these are not the shapes of the pictures, because the vidicon tube scans a square area which is inscribed in the circular field of the lens. As a consequence, the photographed areas of the earth are shaped like a square pincushion, a distorted diamond, or a truncated shape if part of the field is off the earth (Figure 4.2). A satellite system that directs the camera axis straight downward for every picture simplifies the problem of rectification; that is, most of the distortions introduced by the viewing geometry are removed. This is one of the advantages of the Nimbus and the wheel TIROS spacecraft.

If the camera were looking straight down at the North or South Pole, it would be easy to put latitude and longitude lines on the picture. The pole would be at the center of the picture; latitude lines would be concentric circles around the pole; and longitudes would be straight lines radiating from the center point at the pole. Figure 4.3 shows how the geographic grid lines (latitude and longitude)

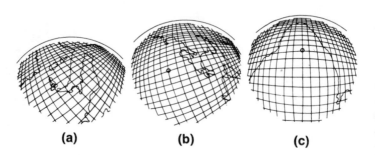

(a)   **(b)**   **(c)**

Figure 4.3 Geographical grids for pictures taken from different angles. The picture center is marked by O, (a) Center at 40° north, 15° east. North to upper right (Italy). (b) Center at 44° north, 63° west. North to right (Nova Scotia). (c) Center at 18° north, 77° east. North to bottom (India). (Courtesy of ESSA.)

must be fitted to pictures taken at various angles from the vertical and at different places over the earth. It is obvious that fitting each picture with a geographic grid is a time consuming job, and the more accurate the fit, the more time is needed.

The earliest method used at the data acquisition stations for gridding each picture consisted of five separate steps. This method is described as an example of the many details to be considered even in this rather straightforward process. First, a positive 35 mm picture transparency was placed in a photo enlarger, and the picture was projected on a focus sheet to obtain the proper degree of enlargement. Then a specially constructed transfer grid, called a *perspective grid*, was substituted for the focus sheet. At this point the picture elements were transferred by hand to a rectangular grid having lines corresponding to those of the perspective grid. A special Mercator chart, on the same scale as the rectangular grid, was then placed over the rectangular grid on a glass-topped table lighted from below. Next, the cloud elements were transferred by hand from the rectangular grid to corresponding positions on a standard weather map. This and the following method of picture rectification are illustrated schematically in Figure 4.4.

Since this was so time consuming, an improved method was developed. The geographic grid lines for each picture were computed ahead of time, using the predicted location and attitude of the satellite at the exact time each picture was to be taken. Electronic computers at the read-out stations were fed this advance information. The computer than calculated and automatically drew the 5° latitude-longitude grids for each picture. Then, when the pictures came in from the satellite, photographic prints enlarged to the proper size to fit the precomputed grids were quickly made. The photographs were placed on top of the grids on a glass-topped table lighted from below, and the grids were drawn in ink directly on the photographs. The photos were fitted together into a rough mosaic, and a nephanalysis was made in a single transfer from the mosaic to a weather map. This method, too, has been replaced by complete handling by a computer.

The computer method of rectification involves digitizing each spot on a television picture in the form of a number to represent brightness. Anywhere from six to ten shades of gray are used in brightness

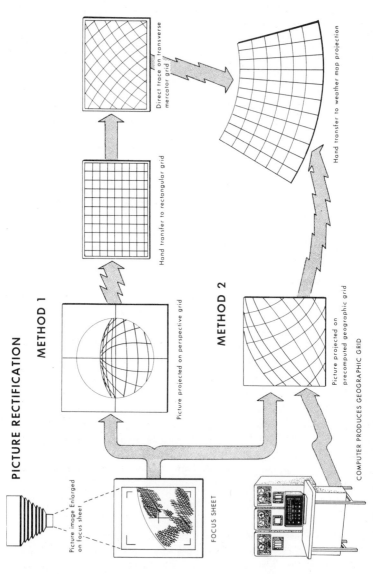

Figure 4.4(a) Schematic diagram of early rectification methods. (Photo, courtesy of ESSA.)

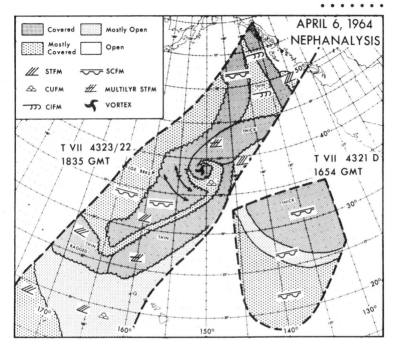

Figure 4.4(b) A typical nephanalysis. (Photo, courtesy of ESSA.)

coding. Then each spot—there are over one-half million per picture—
is located on a map and printed by the computer. The result is a
slightly degraded cloud picture which can be transmitted by ordinary
facsimile (Figure 4.5). The computer can handle a whole sequence
of pictures to produce a cloud picture mosaic superimposed on a
standard map. In this way a picture mosaic ready for use by the
receiving meteorologist rather than a schematic analysis can be transmitted. These mosaics provide much more detail than the schematic
nephanalyses previously used.

The infrared data from the TIROS satellite present a more difficult
processing problem. The data from the five channel radiometer, men-

Figure 4.5 Facsimile transmission of digitally produced cloud map of the Tropics from 10° W to 120° W and from 30° N to 30° S. Irregularly shaped blank areas are places where the satellite did not photograph the clouds. This map was made from the televised signals of 72 pictures transmitted by ESSA 1 on July 21, 1966. (Photo, courtesy of ESSA.)

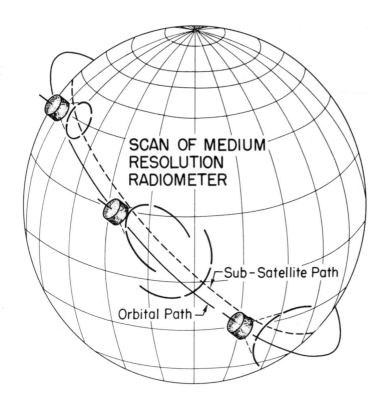

Figure 4.6 Scan patterns of the five-channel radiometer. (Courtesy of NASA.)

tioned in Chapters 2, 3, and 5, reach the ground in the form of analog signals; the data are represented by modulation to the basic carrier frequency. The radiometer itself is mounted at an angle of 45° to the spin axis of TIROS and looks out of both the bottom and side of the satellite. The scan patterns (Figure 4.6) are the result of the satellite's spinning motion (12 revolutions per minute) and its forward motion in orbit (17,000 miles per hour).

These data, recorded on magnetic tape as they are received, can

. . . .

either be transmitted directly to a data processing center for immediate interpretation, or the tapes can be airmailed to a processing center for the precise listing and analyses described below. The immediate use of radiation data involves accepting certain gross approximations in the measurements, and consequently using the mapped data as fields of relative, rather than exact, measurements. The meteorologist could thereby distinguish areas that were warmer or colder than their surroundings, but he would not know the temperatures of those areas very accurately.

The instantaneous field of view of the medium resolution sensor (such as that carried on some of the TIROS) is about 5°. If it views straight downward, this encompasses a circle on the earth about 30 miles in diameter, or correspondingly larger areas when the sensor axis is tilted. A very large number of individual measurements are recorded during the time the scan spot is moving a distance of 30 miles across the earth's surface. For that reason the radiation record is virtually continuous and represents radiation from greatly overlapping areas. To reduce the data to manageable proportions, the record is sampled about 15 times per second.* This is an adequate set of measurements for most meteorological purposes. The processing of the radiation data consists of converting the sampled data points from analog to digital form, so they can be processed by a computer. Then each datum point is located exactly in time and space. A final meteorological radiation tape is made, in which the time, location, tilt angle between the "look angle" and the vertical, and the intensity of the radiation in watts per square meter for each spot are listed. This is the basic material used to convert these data to maps showing the areas of low and high emittance. The five radiation channels originally used on the early TIROS measured, respectively, the emission of energy from the top of the water vapor in the atmosphere (6.0 to 6.5 micron wavelengths), emissions in the "window" (8 to 12 microns), reflected solar radiation (0.2 to 6.0 microns), total infrared radiation emitted by the earth and its atmosphere (7 to 30

---

* This rate of sampling was commenced with TIROS VII. The earlier records were sampled about 8 times per second.

microns), and reflected solar radiation in the visible region of the spectrum (0.55 to 0.75 microns). This last measurement can be used as a check on the television cameras by comparing maps of radiation from this channel with the cloud pictures taken at the same time. Maps of the radiation from the 8 to 12 micron channel can show us the location of clouds and clear areas, the temperatures of the earth, the oceans, and the cloud tops, and can be used to find the height of the tops of overcast clouds as discussed in Chapter 6.

5

• • • •

Satellite Data in

Daily Forecasting

Only TIROS weather satellites were used from 1960 through 1965. While the pictures were useful, the use to which they were put was a matter of fortuity rather than of routine. Even during periods when two satellites were in operation, days would go by when pictures of the areas of greatest weather activity were not available. The meteorologists could not depend on having pictures when needed. This lack of routine availability inherent in the TIROS system has been discussed fully in Chapter 3.

For true operational use, satellite data must be available as routinely as conventional weather observations, that is, at regular intervals and over the same areas day after day. An operational system must provide data at fixed times each day; the viewing angle must be as close to the vertical as possible; and pictures from each orbit must overlap those from the previous orbit so that a space-continuous view of cloud patterns is available. The operational system now used to replace the initial TIROS system provides pictures of each area of the earth taken at the same local sun time each day. This is done by using a sun-synchronous orbit which brings the satellite as far north and south as 80° of latitude. Pictures are taken only when the camera is pointed as nearly as possible straight down. And finally, the satellites are flown at altitudes sufficiently high to permit overlapping of the pictures from orbit to orbit with zenith angles* no greater than 65°. The vidicon scanning, originally 500 lines per picture, has been increased to 800 lines to obtain better resolution in the pictures. Eventually, as many as 1,500 lines will be used to further increase the resolution of picture elements.

Despite the disadvantages of the TIROS system, the pictures were used operationally from the first transmissions. Prior to the launch of TIROS I, the meteorologists involved in the project realized that, should the television cameras work as planned, a definite system for producing a cloud map (nephanalysis) would be required if the pictures were to be immediately useful. The recognition of this need led to the development of an immediate operational use (IOU) plan which provided for rectification of the pictures, representation of the cloud systems on a standard map projection, and quick transmission of the nephanalyses to the users.

Starting with TIROS I, the pictures were "nephed," or used to make cloud maps which were transmitted by facsimile to an ever growing number of weather stations. The first few nephanalyses were subjected to much careful scrutiny both in the United States and abroad. By the middle of June, 1960, a little more than three months after the first TIROS launch, there was general agreement that

---

* Zenith angle is the angle measured from the earth's surface between the local vertical and the satellite.

weather satellites could furnish useful information on the distribution of clouds over the earth and could provide a means for routine surveillance of developing and moving storms.

Since TIROS I, the IOU plan has been constantly revised to decrease the delay between receipt of the pictures on the ground and receipt of the nephanalysis by the users. Rectification procedures were simplified, location accuracy increased, and more meaningful schematic representations of cloud patterns devised. Communications procedures were improved and expanded. In addition to the schematic nephanalyses, a limited number of actual pictures from each sequence were sent by photofacsimile, at first only to NASA and to the National Meteorological Center at Suitland, Maryland, and then later to forecast centers in the United States and occasionally to the meteorological services of England, Australia, France, and other countries. The nephanalyses themselves were eventually broadcast to other countries by radiofacsimile. Nephanalyses are put into a numerical code format and sent out on international weather communications networks for reception at locations not equipped with radiofacsimile receivers. Even this nephanalysis code was revised as operations continued; the coded message was condensed to about one-third of its original length to save transmission time on the nearly saturated weather networks.

The effectiveness of any operational system depends on its meeting the needs of its users. Since the TIROS satellites could not always photograph the areas where pictures were needed, a great deal of advance planning was necessary. Users were advised of the areas that could be photographed in the next 24 to 48 hours and of areas where photography might be possible during the next 7 to 10 days. Using this information, operational meteorologists and experimenters could request pictures over specific areas. These requests were honored to the fullest extent possible. During the operations of TIROS I through VIII, special pictures were taken in support of hurricane and tropical storm reconnaissance and for scientific investigations such as the International Indian Ocean Expedition, Project TIREC (the Joint United States and Canadian ice reconnaissance program), and the Equatorial Atlantic Expedition. The Mercury and Gemini flights and many other projects used satellite photographs for planning their launches and for information on the weather in re-entry and landing areas.

In some parts of the world, the satellite pictures furnish the only available clue to existing weather patterns. For example, storms can form and reach full fury in lonely unobserved regions of the South Indian Ocean. A week or more can go by before such a storm gives forewarning of its presence and impending movement onto the land. Storms here and in other parts of the world can be spotted in the satellite pictures and warnings sent to inhabited areas likely to be affected. Such a warning service was established during the lifetime of TIROS III. Bulletins are sent out within 2 hours after the satellite photographs the storm. Since July of 1961, thousands of flash advisories on tropical storms and other potentially hazardous weather conditions have been sent to United States installations and to the weather services of more than 50 other nations.

The discovery and tracking of tropical storms, hurricanes, and typhoons is one of the more spectacular of the operational uses of weather satellites. On July 12, 1961, TIROS III, destined to be known as the "hurricane hunter" satellite, was launched. The first hurricane sighted by TIROS III was ANNA. This storm was identified on July 19, and was followed as it moved from the coast of Venezuela to British Honduras, where it finally dissipated four days later. ANNA also aroused the curiosity of the meteorological researchers. They tracked ANNA backward across the Atlantic using satellite photographs and found the weak cloud arrangement at 10°N, 39°W, about in the middle of the tropical Atlantic, that eventually became ANNA. They noted how its structure changed from day to day until a mature hurricane had developed.

By the spring of 1964, hundreds of pictures of hurricanes and typhoons had been studied in detail. From these studies a method was developed for estimating the maximum winds of a storm from its size and appearance on a satellite photograph. A nomogram was developed that relates the size of the storm (measured in degrees of latitude) and the appearance of its spiral cloud bands with a maximum wind speed. Figure 5.1 shows the nomogram and sketches of

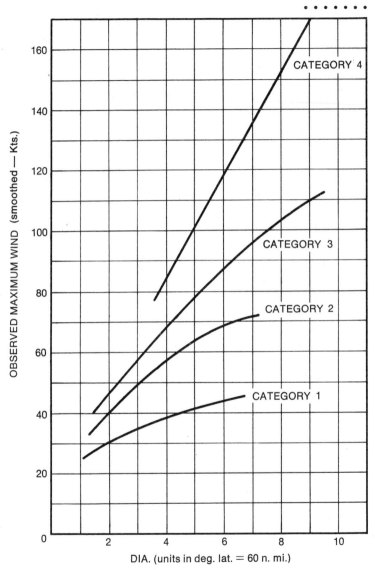

Figure 5.1(a) Chart used to estimate maximum winds of a hurricane or typhoon.

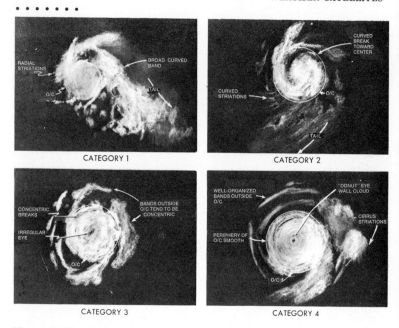

CATEGORY 1

CATEGORY 2

CATEGORY 3

CATEGORY 4

Figure 5.1(b) Drawing used to illustrate characteristic pattern at different storm intensities (categories). (Photo, courtesy of ESSA.)

various band structures (categories). This experimental method was used operationally in the summer and fall of 1964, with good results. The maximum wind forecasts were checked against wind speeds measured by reconnaissance aircraft. The average error was 15 knots and the maximum error 25 knots. Some estimates were within 5 knots of the actual wind speed. Figure 5.2 shows a satellite photograph of hurricane CLEO taken on August 26, 1964. The wind speeds of this storm estimated by the experimental method were 65 knots; the reconnaissance aircraft measurement was 65 knots; and the detailed post-analysis also showed 65 knots!

As a result of these studies, a procedure has been developed to use weather satellites as routine surveillance vehicles. When a mass of clouds in a satellite photograph is identified as a possible focal

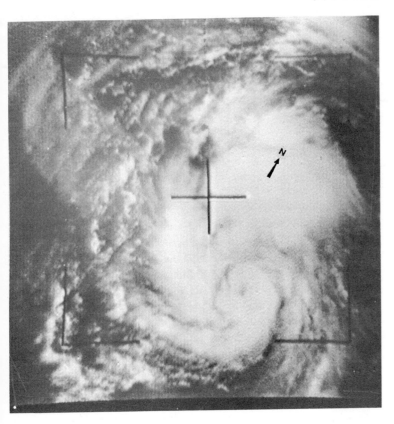

Figure 5.2 Hurricane Cleo on August 26, 1964. The measured diameter of this storm was 3° of latitude; the category (see Figure 5.1) was 3. The maximum winds were estimated to be 65 knots. (Photo, courtesy of ESSA.)

point for the development of a tropical storm, aircraft are sent to investigate. This procedure will eventually replace the older practice of having weather reconnaissance aircraft fly routine tracks day after day with the hope that a developing storm will not slip through their surveillance net. This use of the weather satellites provides more effective storm surveillance and also greatly reduces costly routine reconnaissance by aircraft. Since 1961 satellites have sighted and tracked almost all the dangerous storms of the tropics in all parts of the world where they occur: the Atlantic, the North and South Pacific, and the Indian Ocean both north and south of the equator.

The nephanalyses have also been used as maps depicting weather conditions along transoceanic aerial routes. Weather along such routes as between New York and Dakar (Senegal), San Francisco and Hawaii, Miami and Belem (Brazil), and Hawaii and Fiji is poorly observed from the earth's surface because of the lack of land stations, shipping, or any conventional reporting systems. The satellite pictures can and do show much detail on the cloud distribution along these routes. One reaction to the satellite data came from an airline pilot who was given a TIROS nephanalysis as part of his weather briefing for a flight from New York to Dakar. In part he said "From 60° West to Dakar, the map [nephanalysis] was so accurate as to be almost unbelievable. The map position of the cold front was not only located exactly, but with a 150 mile scan on radar its northeast-southwest positioning was clearly definable. The cloud types and amounts were completely correct. . . In my estimation we have found the answer, let's send up more TIROS."

Many weather phenomena* can be associated with the type of clouds that are seen in satellite photographs (Figures 5.3 through 5.5). Very bright, clearly defined, isolated cloud patches have been identified as associated with severe thunderstorms and sometimes tornadoes. Distinctive patterns of cirrus clouds have been associated with the jet stream and can be used to locate the high speed jet stream winds. In addition, they also are a clue to the possible presence of the unseeable clear air turbulence that can be so dangerous to high flying aircraft.

A rather attractive ripplelike pattern has been identified with clouds known to result from mountain waves. These are strong winds that form standing waves† in the lee of mountains, which could be dangerous to any plane that wanders into their influence. Light planes

---

* Many of the following phenomena are treated in detail in Chapter 6.
† See p. 91.

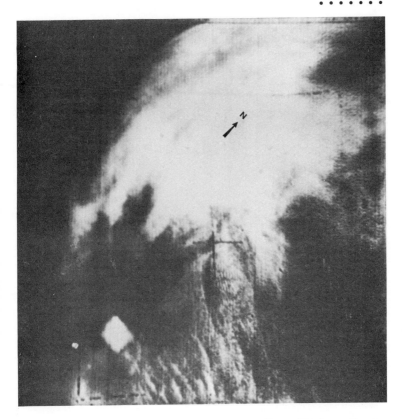

Figure 5.3 "Square" cloud photographed over Texas-Oklahoma border on May 19, 1960. This cloud was approximately 100 miles on a side. As the cloud mass moved to the northeast, hail, heavy thunderstorms, and tornadoes were reported. (Photo, courtesy of ESSA.)

would be tossed about like playing cards and heavy planes subjected to severe turbulence.

A somewhat more benign phenomenon than the standing wave pattern is the cellular pattern of cumulus clouds seen in many satellite pictures. These circles or semicircles, ranging from 10 to 90 miles in diameter, indicate the presence of convective activity from the surface

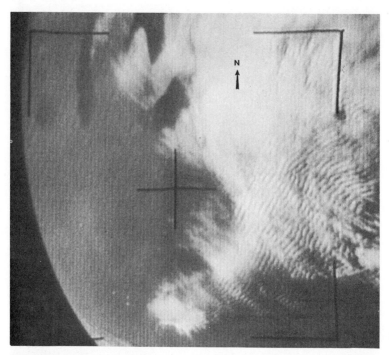

Figure 5.4 Wave clouds over and east of the Appalachians. TIROS VII photograph taken on April 9, 1964. (Photo, courtesy of ESSA.)

to perhaps as high as 10,000 feet. In this layer there are cumulus clouds and bumpy air for aircraft. Above, the flying is smooth. All the previous phenomena and others are being studied in detail, first to determine the physical causes of the phenomena, and then to develop methods to make use of this knowledge in operational forecasting.

Operational methods for using radiation measurements are under development. One way the infrared data can be used is to map the positions of large cloud masses at night. The measurements used to determine the temperatures of cloud tops can also be employed to furnish upper air temperatures over areas where the data are sparse.

Figure 5.5 Cellular patterns in a low cloud several hundred miles southwest of the Galapagos Islands. The ringlike patterns at the upper left are similar to laboratory convective patterns. (Photo, courtesy of ESSA.)

The presence of snow over remote areas and the distribution of ice on navigable rivers and coastal shipping lanes could also be mapped by the use of infrared measurements. With a special infrared sensor, the vertical temperature structure of the higher levels of the atmosphere can be measured daily and used by the meteorologist in his analysis and forecasting procedures (Figure 5.6). In brief, the satellite data are used operationally to locate and identify significant weather patterns for use by the weather forecaster in his daily operations.

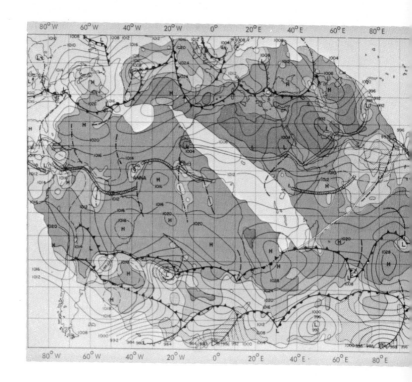

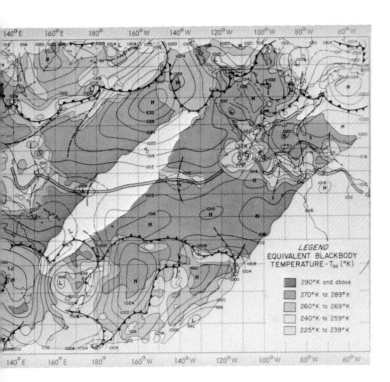

Figure 5.6 Map of "window" radiation (8 to 12 microns) from TIROS III, on July 16, 1961. The darkest areas represent warm temperatures, hence few or no clouds. Areas where no data were obtained are completely un-shaded. (Photo, courtesy of NASA.)

6

Use of Satellite

Data in Research

Satellite data are particularly valuable to researchers because some of the measurements can be made from no other platform. Research has progressed more rapidly with pictures than with infrared data since many problems associated with infrared measurements had to be solved before the data were in usable form. Television pictures from satellites are available almost immediately after the signals are received; radiation measurements, on the other hand, must go through involved processing before they can be displayed as maps of radiation intensity or effective temperatures.

Figure 6.1
High resolution infrared (HRIR) "picture" from Nimbus I, taken about midnight on September 2, 1964. The brightest areas are clouds (cold temperatures); the darkest areas are warm lakes and the ocean. This strip extends from about the equator to southern Canada and is approximately 1,000 miles wide. Despite the great distortion, the following features can be seen: The Gulf of Baja California (dark area near the center); the black specks at the left of the center are lakes, and the largest is Lake Tahoe; the clouds (bright areas) in the bottom part of the upper half are associated with a frontal system extending westward from the Dakotas; the large cloud mass near the bottom is a tropical storm. (Photo, courtesy of NASA.)

With the launch of Nimbus in late 1964, a method was introduced to represent radiation measurements in the form of pictures. "Pictures" like the sample shown in Figure 6.1 can be used almost as if they were made with visible light, but still, a mapping of the radiation in digital form is necessary for much of the research with infrared data.

It would seem that these new data from satellites could be used immediately to shed light on the unsolved problems of meteorology. While this has been done insofar as possible, scientific gains are not so easily and simply won. The reason is that these new data require extensive study before they can be used. To illustrate this point, it was noticed that as the ever growing accumulation of pictures was studied, certain distinctive cloud patterns were seen repeatedly. Many of these patterns were completely new to meteorologists because they occurred on a scale too large to be seen by an observer on the ground or in an aircraft. Many patterns, unknown before the space age, soon became familiar and recognizable at a glance (e.g., Figure 5.5). Their repeated occurrence indicated the recurrence of the specific set of atmospheric conditions that caused them. These patterns thus gave promise of revealing the existence of some of the same variables that the analyst derives from plotting weather maps and analyzing routine weather observations. The problem was to discover *what* combination of conditions produced the various patterns; this is one of the research tasks.

The problems are not straightforward. The researcher was accustomed to using direct measurements of wind, temperature, and moisture in his studies; these new data gave him none of these. Rather, he was faced with cloud patterns which were the *result* of wind, temperature, and moisture interaction; the pictures show results, not the causes. The research worker thus had to take a look at these phenomena from a new point of view. Instead of starting with the ingredients, he had to analyze the end products and deduce the ingredients.

Research with satellite data falls into two separate but interacting classes. One is the development of techniques for applying satellite data to operational use. The recognition of patterns that reveal the

• • • • • • •

beginning of new storms is an example of direct operational use, a
is the deduction of wind direction from cloud forms. The other clas
of research serves to extend our understanding of atmospheric physics
Some of the latter results may not be applicable to current operations
but each extension of knowledge is yet another piece to the puzzl
that will eventually expand the use of satellite data. Both classes o
research are illustrated in the examples discussed in the remainder o
this chapter; the manner in which they interact will be apparent

A good example of interaction is the case of a simple operationa
question that opened a whole avenue of investigation. A study to se
if cloud bands might be used as indicators of wind direction reveale
that in some cases they showed the configuration of the temperatur
field instead. Figure 6.2 is a picture from TIROS IV showing
cyclonic cloud pattern over the midwest. The black spiked symbo
marks the approximate center of the cloud pattern. This location is
suggested especially by the loosely organized curved array of cloud
groups south of the center. The white triangle marks the position o
the actual circulation center that was determined from simultaneous
wind observations. The separation between these centers was about
150 miles. Investigation of the winds at several levels from the bottom
to the top of the cloud layer showed that the pattern was curved along
the vertical *shear vectors* in the cloud layer.

When the wind changes with height, the shear vector is that vector
which must be add vectorially to the lower wind to arrive at the vector
representing the upper wind. A vector addition of this type is illustrated in Figure 6.3. Now, in the atmosphere the wind blows along
isobars so that the low pressure is to the left of an observer facing
downstream (in the Northern Hemisphere). When the wind changes
direction with height, it is because the isobars change direction. Such
a change is the consequence of a horizontal temperature variation in
the air layer. It can be shown that the vertical shear vector is parallel
to the mean isotherms of the layer involved. Isotherms are lines
connecting points of equal temperature. Therefore, the curved bands
of Figure 6.2 delineate the orientation of the temperature field, not
the flow field.

This effect is similar to the action of an overturning fluid in the

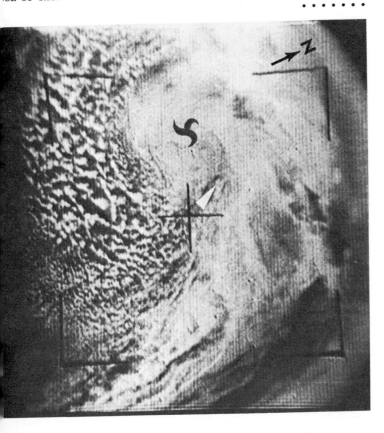

Figure 6.2 A curved cloud pattern centered over central South Dakota (spiked symbol) produced by a cyclone center over south-central Minnesota (white triangle) on March 31, 1962. (Photo, courtesy of ESSA.)

hydrodynamics laboratory. Both theory and experiments with flowing fluids have shown that a stirred layer will organize its upward and downward motion in long bands along the shear vector. In the atmosphere, the stirring motion is supplied by the convection of cumulus clouds. Apparently the laboratory model is a good analog of this atmospheric phenomenon and suggests that the theory which was

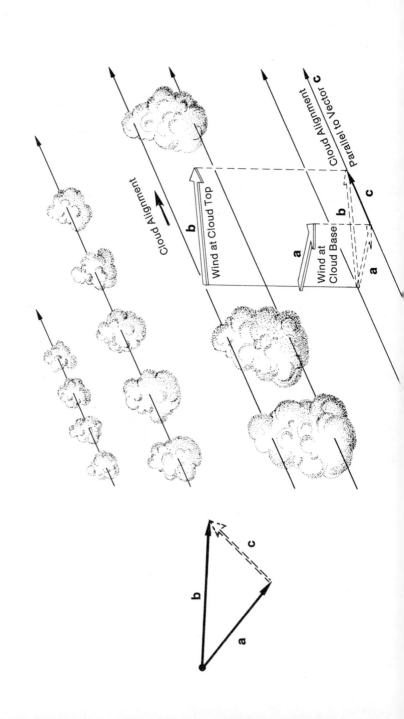

developed and checked in the laboratory can be applied to the atmosphere.

In this example the meteorologist sought the answer he needed to an operational question in order to draw a wind analysis where he had only cloud pictures. The answer, "Cloud bands do not always lie along the flow," leaves him with another question, "Under what conditions may the arrays be interpreted as temperature lines and when as wind lines?" The researcher is thus confronted with a new task. At the present time only a partial answer has been found to this question. Much more research into the basic nature of the atmosphere must be completed before these problems are completely solved.

While some investigations lead to additional questions, satellite pictures can also provide some very direct and simple results. For example, the predilection of the atmosphere to arrange its zones of upward motion and its moisture-rich areas into bands has long challenged the atmospheric scientists. In order to obtain a description of this tendency in previous years, thousands of rainfall records were carefully analyzed. The task was difficult because the bands are relatively narrow. As they are carried past a rain gauge, the precipitation from one band is added to that of its predecessor, thus blurring the pattern. But a glance at a picture of such a system reveals the dimensions of the bands, their spacing, and their degree of organization.

In addition to the type of picture interpretation just discussed, there is another kind of useful information. First, for background it is necessary to explain the terms used. Two fundamental properties of fluid motion are *vorticity* and *divergence*. These two characteristics of fluid motion are important because their interaction is intimately linked with the flow of air over the earth's surface and with the development of cloud patterns. Vorticity is the "spin" of each

Figure 6.3 (Opposite) An illustration of vector addition and its application to the orientation of cloud rows. On the left, vector *a* + vector *c* = vector *b*. On the right, *a* represents the wind vector at the cloud base, *c* the shear vector which must be added to *a* to obtain the vector *b*, which represents the wind vector at the cloud top. The orientation of the cloud rows is along *c*.

small column of fluid about its vertical axis.* This spin is caused by the curvature of the flow plus its lateral shear, that is, the cross-stream change of wind speed. It is easy to visualize that a column of air will twist if one side moves faster than the other. Such motion can be due either to shearing or curved flow.

Divergence is the amount a given volume of air is being depleted by differential flow. Let us consider a layer of fluid moving through an imaginary box. Imagine that the fluid flows faster out of the downstream side than it flows into the upstream side. The fluid within the box is thus being depleted and is said to be *diverging*. The consequence of this horizontal divergence is to decrease the depth of the fluid in the box. Negative divergence, sometimes called *convergence*, is the opposite effect; fluid accumulates in the box because the inflow is faster than the outflow. Despite the fact that there are no fixed "boxes" in the atmosphere, a given region can accumulate air by horizontal convergence, and the excess mass is forced to rise.

The atmosphere moves across the earth's surface largely in horizontal flow, but some divergence and vorticity is always imposed. (Part of the vorticity is imparted from the earth's rotation.) If it were not for divergence and convergence and the resulting downward and upward vertical motions, there could be no weather because upward motion is required to form clouds and precipitation. Where the air converges and rises, the laws of hydrodynamics force it to spin faster, much as a spinning figure skater rotates faster when he draws in his arms. As a consequence, a weather disturbance is also the site of concentrated spin.

While clouds are carried along by the wind, it is the divergence and vorticity that produce and shape the cloud patterns. Therefore, cloud patterns have great potential for revealing the location and intensity of these weather producing properties. Tropical storm† intensity can be estimated by measuring the size of the storm cloud canopy

---

* Rigorously, vorticity is spin about each of three mutually perpendicular axes, but in many problems of meteorology, only spin about the vertical axis is significant.

† Violent tropical storms are called "hurricanes" in the Atlantic and "typhoons" in the central to western Pacific.

 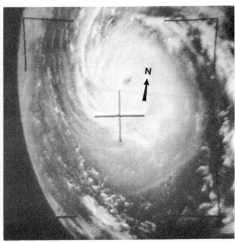

Figure 6.4 Typhoon Amy on August 29, 1962 (left) and on August 31, 1962 (right) moving toward the west, north of the island of Guam. The greatest wind speed on the 29th was 45 knots, and on the 31st was 95 knots. Clues to the increased intensity can be seen in the increased circular organization and the appearance of the storm eye (the small dark area near the central **+** on the right). (Photo, courtesy of ESSA.)

and classifying its degree of pattern organization. Typhoon AMY is shown in two different stages of intensity in Figure 6.4. On the left, the maximum rotary winds were 45 knots, while on the right, the storm contained wind speeds up to 95 knots. The sharp-edged, nearly circular bands indicate the greater concentration of spin associated with the stronger circulation (see also Figure 5.1).

Researchers are studying other spiral arrays to formulate techniques for estimating the magnitude of divergence and vorticity associated with various storms. These quantities would be directly usable in forecasting. Some progress has already been made. As an illustration, Figure 6.5 shows two cyclones which are the same type as the one in Figure 6.2. While all three storms have the characteristic spiral pattern, careful examination will show that the shapes of the partly

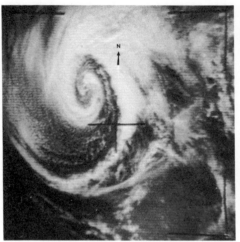 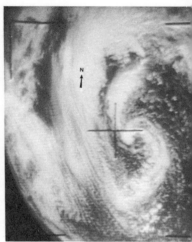

Figure 6.5 A North Atlantic cyclone on (left) February 16, and (right) February 17, 1965. The change of the sharp-edged spirals on the left to the fuzzy pattern on the right is evidence that the storm is decreasing in intensity. (Photos, courtesy of ESSA.)

clouded streaks are different. Research has demonstrated that these differences reveal, in part, the intensity and stage of development of the storms. In its early stages, the storm forces air upward to form large areas of dense cloudiness. The area of enhanced cloudiness may be hundreds of miles across, but no vigorous circular motion has developed so there is little visible pattern. As more air rises and more spin is generated, the clouds are swept into curved bands. The different patterns are the result of the length of time this process has existed. Eventually, the energy is exhausted and the storm "runs down." Upward vertical motion stops; friction destroys the circulation; and the pattern disappears. The vortexlike pattern in Figure 6.5, at the left, shows a mature storm. The dark spiral is air that has been dried by descent and swept almost completely around the storm center. In about 2 days this storm will commence to run down and will have the irregular pattern of Figure 6.5, at the right.

The common means of calculating a wind field where no actual observations of wind exist is to compute the wind from the isobar spacing of the measured pressure pattern. If vorticity and divergence are known, it is also possible to derive the wind field by solving certain equations with a high speed electronic computer. Techniques to interpret cloud patterns in terms of their vorticity and divergence pattern are under investigation. If such techniques can be perfected, the horizontal wind field can be computed just as easily as if pressure measurements were used. Learning to interpret the patterns of all types of storms in terms of the *magnitude* of physical quantities continues to be an important and difficult research task.

While studies concerning storms were being pursued, meteorologists came across other cloud patterns that were not produced by traveling storms. Sometimes the responsible phenomenon was already known, but others were new and strange. An example of a known mechanism is the mountain waves of Figure 6.6. Figure 6.7, on the other hand, shows eddies, produced by mountainous islands, that were undetected before the space age. Eddies similar in their behavior and geometry have been produced in the laboratory. Studies based on this similarity have already yielded some understanding of the phenomenon, but the differences still leave much work to be done on this problem.

Even pictures of familiar mechanisms yield significant research results. For example, a theory has been developed to account for mountain waves, which relates the atmospheric stability and wind speed to their wavelength. Under proper conditions, air forced to flow over a barrier such as a mountain does not move smoothly downwind from the ridge. Rather, it has an up and down motion quite similar to the wavy surface of disturbed water. Moisture condenses to clouds in the upward motion and evaporates in the downward motion, so that long lines of clouds mark the wave crests, and the clear spaces between the lines mark the wave troughs. Pictures such as Figure 6.6 thus reveal the wavelength. When this pattern is photographed over areas where standard observations are made, the theory can be checked. Where the theory and observations do not agree, the theory must be modified and improved. The improved

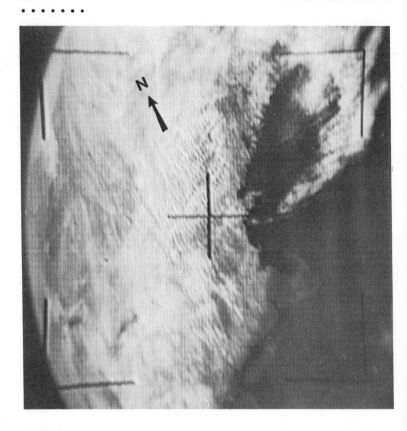

Figure 6.6 Mountain wave clouds pictured over New England on March 7, 1963 by TIROS V, looking toward the western horizon. Long Island, New York, and Cape Cod, Massachusetts, can be seen in the lower right quadrant. (Photo, courtesy of ESSA.)

results are valuable because they contribute to our understanding of complex atmospheric behavior.

Radiation data can be used directly in operations and in research problems. In some ways infrared data are superior to pictures because they provide quantitative measurements. Let us review some

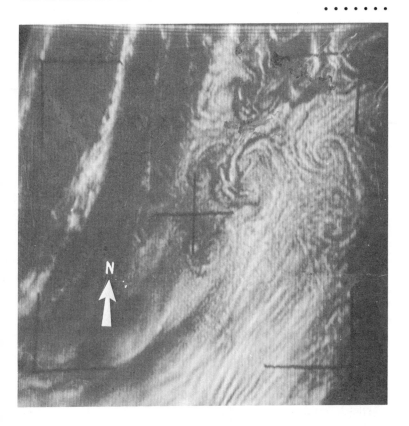

Figure 6.7 Small scale eddies in low stratus clouds in the eastern Atlantic, downstream from the mountainous islands of Madeira and the Canaries. (Photo, courtesy of ESSA.)

characteristics of infrared radiation which enable us to derive magnitudes of the measured quantities. The intensity of radiation from any substance increases greatly as its temperature increases. A temperature increase of only 1 per cent produces a radiation increase of 4 per cent. In addition to temperature effects, the intensity of radiation is influenced by the "efficiency" of the substance as a radiator. If a substance is 100 per cent efficient, it is called a "black body" radiator, and it will absorb and emit radiation with equal efficiency. Such substances are said to have an absorption coefficient of 1.0. If another substance is only 50 per cent efficient as an absorber and an emitter, it will have an absorption coefficient of 0.5. Since the radiation sensors measure only the magnitude (intensity) of radiation, it is necessary to know the absorption coefficient of the radiating substance in order to derive its temperature from the satellite radiation measurements. When we say that the "effective radiating temperature" of a substance, derived from its radiation, is $X°$, we mean that a black body at $X°$ would radiate energy at the observed intensity.

The atmosphere does not absorb all wavelengths with equal efficiency.* Only a small part of the visible wavelengths are absorbed by the atmosphere. On the other hand, the longer infrared wavelengths are largely absorbed by the water vapor and carbon dioxide in the atmosphere. At certain intervals in the infrared, however, water vapor is almost transparent, absorbing very little radiation (Figure 2.1). The principal "window" through the atmospheric water vapor is in the range from 8 to 12 microns.

In order to take advantage of these features of atmospheric transmission, some satellite radiometers are designed to measure radiation intensity in these window wavelengths; others measure the total infrared long-wave radiation over the range from about 7 to 40 microns. The wide range radiometer gives a good measurement of the total long-wave radiation lost from the earth to space. Such data are used in studies of the heat budget of our planet.

The operational use of infrared mapping of cloud-top temperatures with the window data has already been described. The data are also of immense potential for research, supplying information not available from television pictures. For example, important unsolved problems of hurricane formation can be studied with infrared data. The hurricane always develops from a pre-existing disturbance over tropi-

---

* A discussion of this characteristic is found in Chapter 2 under "electromagnetic radiation."

cal waters. There are many such disturbances, but only a few inten-
sify to dangerous hurricane strength. The intensification stage may
be associated with the rapid development of convective clouds that
produce cold ice clouds as they push upward toward the stratosphere.
Just at the critical stage, the developing ice clouds and the dense
clouds of middle levels may look very much alike on television pictures. However, a careful surveillance with infrared measurement
may detect the changing character of high cold clouds and furnish
clues about the intensification of these storms.

Cloud-top radiation must be measured in the water vapor windows,
but radiation at other wavelengths is also important for research.
The invisible water vapor in the atmosphere emits its radiation
strongly from about 5.5 to 7.0 microns. It is such an efficient absorber
(and emitter) in these wavelengths, that almost all the radiation from
water vapor that reaches the satellite comes from only the upper part
of the water vapor layers. All radiation emitted from lower layers of
moisture is reabsorbed by the overlying water vapor. The radiating
temperature of vapor is therefore the temperature at the top of the
moisture layers in the atmosphere. Where the upper air is dry, the
low-lying vapor layer radiates at a high temperature, but where
moisture exists at high altitudes, the cold temperatures associated with
its great altitude are measured. These measurements thus provide a
means of mapping the height of the invisible water vapor in the
atmosphere. To the television camera there is no difference between
a clear area with dry air above it and a clear area with moist air
aloft. However, the difference in water vapor content is of great
importance meteorologically, since moisture-laden air is loaded with
latent energy that can be released to increase a traveling storm's
intensity.

In addition to the importance of latent energy awaiting release,
the amount of radiant energy lost to space is quite different over
regions covered with moist air and those covered with dry air. This
fact brings us to the most significant area of research made possible
by the satellite: the heat budget of our planet earth. Why must meteorologists measure the heat budget? It is already known that the
heating and cooling of the earth is pretty much in a state of equi-

• • • • • • •

librium. If it were not, there would be a year-to-year change of temperature over the entire earth, which is contrary to observation.

The reason we measure infrared energy from the satellite is because this energy source is constant only when averaged over the whole earth season by season. The day-to-day variations are large. The distribution of cloudy and clear areas and of moist and dry regions all affect the heating and cooling of the earth and its atmosphere. Satellite measurement of this variable heating and cooling appears to be the only method of obtaining this information so vital to long-range forecasting.

The physical laws governing the atmosphere are basically those that govern any heat engine. To understand why the engine runs at variable speeds, and to predict those variations, it is necessary to know the amount of work being done, the amount of energy available from the heat source, and the losses suffered when transferring the heat energy from the boiler to the engine. Some of these variables can and are being measured from within the atmosphere. Forecasting has advanced to its present stage by using those measurable quantities. The critical unknown variable is the net amount and variability of solar energy absorbed by the atmosphere. The numerical weather prediction equations up to this time have not taken into account the actual variation of radiation energy. Even though the sun's input of energy at the outer limits of the atmosphere may be relatively constant, the amount of this energy available to the atmosphere is not constant because of the complicated interaction of radiation and weather.

Let us imagine the skies over the entire globe to be unusually cloud-free at some given time. Under those conditions, a large portion of the solar radiation would reach the earth's surface, be absorbed, and much of the resulting long-wave radiation would thus be trapped in the lower atmosphere. This would lead to a great amount of heating at the low latitudes. At the same time, the high latitudes (especially in the winter hemisphere) would lose heat more rapidly than is normal, and a great meridional temperature difference would be established. This is an unstable arrangement in which small disturbances can initiate large north and south air displacement. As the contrasting air masses mixed, violent weather and cloudiness would be produced. The cloudiness would shield the earth from solar radiation, thus shutting off the overnormal input of heat energy to the earth's atmosphere. Eventually, the excess energy accumulated during the cloud-free period would be dissipated by friction so that a period of below normal weather activity would set in. This would lead to clearing skies, and the system would be ready for another cycle.

Such cycles might be as long as several weeks; this is the variability of concern to long range forecasters. The cycle is really much more complicated than the simple train of events just described. The whole atmospheric complex is involved. Under certain initial conditions of flow, a high level of energy must be built up before it becomes unstable and is converted to the kinetic energy of storms. Under other initial conditions, only moderate levels of energy accumulate before they are dissipated by storminess. These complications produce cycles of irregular length and render the time-honored method of statistical cycles a very poor means of long range forecasting.

Thus, since an important part of the long range forecast problem lies in the variable input of energy, satellite data is of prime importance. No other system can collect these data over the entire earth's surface every day. Long range forecasting without measurement of this variable heat balance is as difficult as forecasting the speed of an engine without knowing how the throttle is being manipulated!

Perhaps the most difficult area of research is the quest for techniques of automating the interpretation and incorporation of picture and infrared radiation data into forecasting. Continued progress will depend critically on our ability to make objective analyses of the growing mass of data and to translate them into quantitative information. A computer, given the problem of making numerical forecasts from a set of equations, cannot use qualitative, nonnumerical input. So the essence of this important task is to translate the information contained in cloud patterns and radiation measurements into a language that the computer can use. Work along this line has hardly commenced. At present, only qualitative ideas are involved.

The task ahead is to quantify the connection between cloud cover and upward motion. Attaching *numbers* to these concepts is the goal of such research.

Even more difficult is the development of a method to automate the recognition of clues as to the meteorological significance of cloud patterns. Different stages of storm development are illustrated in Figures 6.2 and 6.5, but it is incredibly complex to teach a computer to recognize the differences between those patterns.

Up to this point we have discussed research being done with the satellite data currently available. Important research is also underway to improve and extend the type of data the satellite can obtain. For example, radiation measurements are being made at the earth's surface and from within the atmosphere by balloon-borne radiometers to correlate with satellite data. Detailed knowledge of the manner in which radiation passes through various layers of the atmosphere, layers of dust, and layers of very thin clouds of ice crystals is vital. The atmospheric physicist and the instrument designer must have this information to interpret the satellite measurements and improve future measurements.

Research and development is also underway to produce more sophisticated instruments. An outstanding device that was first test flown on balloons in 1965 is the infrared spectrometer, which can measure the radiation in very narrow wavelength intervals and will eventually provide measurements of the vertical temperature distribution within the atmosphere. Chapter 7, in which future satellites are discussed, describes this development.

Any discussion of the use of satellite data in research becomes partially obsolete almost as it is being written, because new uses are made every day. The wide-viewing satellite instruments reveal glimpses of events that demand an explanation. Our atmosphere is so complex that the satellite is always bringing to our attention unanswered questions that must be solved before we can understand the interlocking mechanism of our atmospheric heat engine. Only *after* this understanding can we hope to predict and control our gaseous environment.

7

• • • •

The Future of

Weather Satellites

The TIROS series was highly successful, but it was known even before TIROS I was launched that more complete coverage would be needed for a satisfactory system. The wheel TIROS and Nimbus satellites were the first steps in that direction. Although both of these represent significant advances, they have inherent weaknesses that must be overcome for a completely adequate system. The requirement for wider coverage was met by providing a means of pointing the camera and other sensors directly downward so that the maximum area was observed at the most favorable angles.

Nimbus achieves this pointing control by maintaining stability in all three axes. Complete stability relative to the local vertical provides an ideal observation platform, but in its present form, Nimbus is not suitable for an operational system. The stability is obtained by use of gas jets, so when the gas carried on board is expended, the vehicle tumbles and its sensors are then useless. Naturally, systems that depend on expendable fuel have a limited lifetime. An operational satellite requires a very long lifetime in order to keep operating costs reasonable.

The wheel TIROS obtains a downward orientation of its camera axis by rotating the camera in the plane of the orbit and snapping pictures at the proper instant. This design is adequate for a camera sensor, but infrared sensors on this type of vehicle are highly complicated. Furthermore, on this TIROS spacecraft power is extremely limited, a factor which sharply limits the potential of this type of satellite for carrying an increasingly complex array of sensors. The meteorological satellite of the future must be a spacecraft that not only overcomes the shortcomings of the Nimbus and the wheel TIROS, but also has the growth potential to incorporate new sensors and auxiliary equipment.

The present state of technology is adequate to satisfy many of the demands that meteorologists will make of a routine satellite system, but other needs will be met only after considerable advances have been made. Initially, we will consider the requirements that can be satisfied within the next few years, and secondly, the achievements that are theoretically possible, together with the obstacles that lie in the path of their implementation. Finally, we will speculate on future sensors that would be extremely valuable, but for which, at present, there is no existing technology. We emphasize "at present," for a breakthrough in the guise of a new technique or new discovery may point the way even as these words are being read.

What are the requirements of an operational, routine, meteorological satellite? Couched in terms of what is feasible in the near future, we list the following:

(1) A reliable, long-lived system combined with a method of rapid data processing. The satellite delivers a new body of data each time it circles the earth, so all information must be processed

and communicated in an interval no longer than the satellite period.
(2) Complete surveillance of the earth's surface at least once each 24 hours. As satellite data become incorporated routinely into forecasting, observations two to four times per day will be demanded.
(3) Continuous surveillance of parts of the earth's surface by use of earth-synchronous satellites.
(4) Information about cloud height (a) superimposed upon television pictures of clouds or melded into an analysis of cloud distribution and derived from simultaneous television and infrared data, or alternatively (b) from high resolution infrared sensors that can show both cloud distribution and heights.
(5) Television capable of operating with feeble light for photographing clouds in moonlight or in starlight.
(6) A device for distinguishing snow and ice from overlying clouds.
(7) Sensors to measure the vertical distribution of temperature and moisture in the atmosphere.
(8) Instruments able to measure the ozone content of the stratosphere.
(9) Equipment to detect precipitation and thunderstorms.
(10) A system analogous to the Automatic Picture Transmission of the TOS system that can deliver picture and infrared data directly to isolated receiving units.

A review of this list will show that items (1) and (2) are satisfied by the TOS system, and that the early research and development Nimbus can partially satisfy (4) and (7). However, every one of the ten goals can be reached with techniques currently available or under development. Some will be operative before the end of this decade.

A *reliable system* will result from engineering based on a good systems analysis, but a full discussion of these matters is not possible here. In brief, reliability can be insured by a careful system design that incorporates duplicate components on the satellite. It is more economical to provide redundant equipment in a single spacecraft than to launch single system satellites at intervals only a short time apart.

Power to operate the equipment of future spacecraft may not be supplied by chemical batteries because such batteries have a limited lifetime. Eventually, nuclear power must be used unless a completely new power source is developed.

The ultimate satellite must be earth-oriented, but the method of stabilizing the spacecraft must be passive such as one using magnetic or gravitational effects. The lifetime of active stabilization systems that consume a propellant is limited by the amount of propellant that can be carried on the spacecraft.

Rapid data reduction and communication are largely nonmeteorological problems that will yield to computer techniques. The methods have already been discussed in Chapter 5.

The requirement for complete earth coverage involves the geometry of the sensors and the celestial mechanics of orbits, as discussed in Chapter 2. Since it is the horizontal* distribution of various features that is important to meteorology, sensors cannot obtain high quality data if the angle of view is excessively oblique. Data accuracy lost because the field is viewed edge-on is a shortcoming that cannot be overcome by improving the sensor design.

In order to satisfy the requirements for observations more frequent than once per day and once per night, a multiple satellite system will be launched. Two daylight observations per 24 hours could be made by placing two sun-synchronous satellites into orbit, one crossing the daylight side of the earth at 9:00 A.M. and the dark side at 9:00 P.M. local time, and a second vehicle in a 3:00 P.M. and 3:00 A.M. orbit. Such orbits would be highly inclined to the equatorial plane (discussed in Chapter 2) and would bring both polar caps under observation many times per day.

The frequency of low latitude observations can be increased by adding a satellite in an equatorial orbit. A spacecraft orbiting in the equatorial plane at about 900 miles altitude would circle the earth directly above the equator about every 2 hours. At this height the

---

* The *horizontal* distribution of clouds is related to circulation of storms; the horizontal distribution of temperature reveals the character of the moving air masses.

entire tropics and subtropics of both hemispheres would be covered at good viewing angles every 2 hours. All hurricanes and typhoons are born in this latitude belt, so a satellite in an equatorial orbit would maximize observations in a most critical area.

Within the family of equatorial satellites is a special one that may have particular meteorological use—the earth-synchronous satellite. Since a satellite's height influences its period, a height can be chosen so that the orbital period is 24 hours. Launched in the direction of the earth's rotation, this vehicle will have no motion relative to the earth. Hanging above one spot at nearly 23,000 miles above the earth, the instruments could command a wide field of view, keeping most of the hurricane-producing zone of the Atlantic under constant watch.

Before such a satellite can be launched, some research and development to improve sensors is needed. A picture of so vast an area would have to be scanned by a large number of television lines to achieve even moderately good resolution. This increases the power and communications problem. Perhaps a gross resolution would suffice for routine surveillance, but once a storm was detected, a high resolution picture would have to be obtained. This would require an aiming control and something similar to a "zoom" lens. Perhaps the actual field of camera view might be fixed, but the transmitted scan pattern might be confined to a selected small section of the vidicon tube to achieve the zoom feature.

In summary, the most effective coverage for meteorological observations can be obtained by:

(1) Two or more sun-synchronous satellites;

(2) Orbital altitudes near 1,000 nautical miles
   (How this altitude minimizes the viewing angles and improves resolution was discussed in Chapter 2);

(3) Addition of a satellite in an equatorial orbit at 500 to 1,000 miles altitude or 3 or 4 "stationary" satellites at 23,000 nautical mile orbits.

Height information has already been added to a few pictures of cloud distribution by a careful transfer of the "window" radiation measurements onto the television pictures. To be operationally useful, this melding must be done at the same rate as the data are collected. It is inconceivable that this large amount of information could be handled by any means other than high speed computers. Even the electronic computers will be taxed. To meld the infrared and picture data with a digital computer, the information must be represented by digits. The variable signal that produces each television line on the picture tube can be converted into a series of digits, with the signal strength represented by different numbers. For example, a typical picture can be adequately reproduced with, say, ten different shades of gray. The strong signals produced by the brightest part of the image would be assigned the number 10, and the signal corresponding to black on the image would be assigned 1. The picture data could then be read into the computer as a series of numbers together with information associating each brightness digit with its proper position on the image.* The computer can then compute the position on earth from which each "spot" of the image was photographed by use of information of satellite altitude, camera angle, and so forth. These geometric calculations require the use of several complex equations, so the computation of the earth coordinates for each spot entails many computer cycles. A similar sequence of computations must also be performed on the infrared data. A map can then be printed showing the picture element at its proper latitude and longitude. A number representing the radiating temperature or a height estimate based on that temperature could be superimposed on the cloud map. This kind of processing on an operational basis will require a tremendous computer capacity and special programming technique.

The picture and infrared data obtained by Nimbus on a single circuit of the earth would require about 280 million binary digits in order to represent each picture element and infrared measurement. The complicated geometric calculations needed to handle 280 million points per orbit exceeds the capability of the general purpose computer. So special computers designed for this particular task must be

---

* A similar system was used to transmit the Mariner IV pictures of Mars back to earth.

built if such a procedure is to be accomplished every time the satellite circles the earth. Some time can be saved by computation shortcuts and approximations. For example, every tenth point might be located on a map and all the intervening points placed with uniform spacing between the located points. Most of the advantage in the use of special purpose computers is achieved by their extreme specialization—they could do no other job. For such a device it may be possible to combine the speed of the analog computer with the accuracy of the digital computer.

The first steps in automatic data processing have already been taken. Picture data are digitalized and printed on a map. The brightness of each element is represented by a different print character: small dots to reproduce the lighter grays and heavier print characters for darker shades. Maps showing numbers or contoured lines of radiating temperatures are also produced by computer. These two maps, either inspected separately or superimposed, give the meteorologist a good representation of the cloud patterns and their approximate heights. From such experimental and preliminary techniques will develop the methods of representation most useful to the forecaster. The complete satellite system will eventually present to the forecaster only the end product of a complex analysis. The final product must evolve step by step, however, because even the meteorologists do not yet know all the uses that can be made of these data.

Low-light television cameras have already been developed, and further research may adapt them for use on satellites. Mercury and Gemini astronauts have reported that clouds are clearly visible under moonlight. From satellite heights, television cameras cannot yet distinguish the low-light levels and the small contrasts that are discernible to the human eye, but prospects are favorable that cameras can be developed to photograph clouds in moonlight. Nighttime sky glow in the atmosphere constitutes an ever-present obstacle, however. This faint light glows in the ionized layers of the stratosphere and so lies between the satellite and the earth's surface. Very small light contrasts emanating from clouds would therefore be made even smaller by the intervening glow.

A competing system for nighttime cloud detection is the infrared

• • • • • • •

radiometer, similar to the high resolution sensor flown on Nimbus. The principal disadvantage in its use is the low resolution of a radiometer compared with that of a vidicon sensor. Nevertheless, infrared measurements made at night are easily used because contrasts are great between the cold cloud tops and the warm earth surface. At the present time the advantage appears to lie with the infrared sensing of clouds at night. The next 5 years will bring increased use of this system.

Ice and snow might be distinguished from clouds by the degree to which they polarize reflected light. Another valuable tool for making the distinction between snow and clouds is the information contained in the infrared measurements, used to measure effective radiating temperatures of snow and clouds. But such temperature measurements, by themselves, can be ambiguous. The temperature of a snow surface under clear skies can be much colder than that of air a few thousand feet above the surface. At even greater heights the air temperature again decreases. Therefore, air temperature far above the surface might be the same as the temperature of the snow cover at the earth's surface. Clouds, having about the temperature of the air in which they are embedded, could thus be either colder or warmer than the snow surface.

Light reflected from ice and snow is partially polarized, while light reflected from clouds is unpolarized. An optical polarizing filter will attentuate polarized light that lies in a different plane from the polarized plane of the filter. Thus, simultaneous filtered and unfiltered pictures of a mixed snow and cloud field would show different brightness contrasts between the snow and clouds. The clouds would appear relatively brighter than the snow in polarized pictures. If the entire field were snow, the filter picture would be uniformly less bright than the unfiltered picture, indicating the presence of uniformly polarized light from the entire surface. Difficulties inherent in this method are still not completely resolved. For example, new snow has quite different polarizing characteristics than old snow, so a mixture of old and new snow might produce the same effect as a mixed cloud and snow field. Before such experiments can be flown on a satellite, it is necessary to determine just what proportion of light is polarized and reflected upward through the atmosphere. It is known that only a small amount of light is polarized. But can this small amount be detected by television cameras on board a satellite? This question is being studied with rocket-borne cameras exposing film of various characteristics, and also by experiments conducted in the Man-in-Space program.

The vertical distribution of temperature in the atmosphere will be measured by use of a spectrometer. The physics underlying this technique and the method of inferring temperature distribution are too complicated for detailed discussion, but the theory can be described qualitatively.

The sensor used is an infrared spectrometer capable of measuring radiation in extremely narrow frequency intervals. In order to sense the vertical distribution of temperature, it is necessary to measure emission from atmospheric carbon dioxide at different frequencies: one frequency near the band of peak carbon dioxide emission at 15 microns, and four or five other narrow bands just off the peak emission frequency. These data can be used to derive temperate variation along the vertical because of a combination of circumstances that is unique for carbon dioxide. This gas is the strongest emitter of all atmospheric gases in the vicinity of 15 microns. Thus, radiation measured in this band comes almost entirely from carbon dioxide. The amount of the gas at each level in the atmosphere is known with adequate accuracy for using this technique, because carbon dioxide is mixed uniformly throughout the atmosphere.

The intensity of radiation from carbon dioxide depends upon its mass, temperature, and absorption coefficient. The latter, in turn, is different for different pressures and for different radiation wavelengths. Because the absorption coefficient depends upon *both* pressure and wavelength, radiation in a certain frequency interval can be attributed to the carbon dioxide at a known pressure (hence, from a known height) in the atmosphere. The radiation intensity, after taking the absorption coefficient into account, provides a measure of the temperature.

In summary, the method involves measuring radiation at several narrow frequency intervals near the 15-micron carbon dioxide band.

Although carbon dioxide at all levels in the atmosphere contributes some energy to the radiation that reaches the satellite, the largest portion in each interval comes from a known layer (pressure interval) of the atmosphere. The minor contribution of the other layers can be estimated with small error and taken into account. Theoretically, this same principle may also be used to deduce the vertical distribution of moisture. Future research will reveal whether the technique is feasible for moisture soundings.

Ozone measurements are important because the distribution of ozone is a good indication of vertical motion in the stratosphere up to about 35 kilometers (approximately 22 miles). Horizontal motions in the stratosphere can be inferred as well. Ozone is a clue to these motions because of the mechanics of its formation.

Ozone is produced rapidly and destroyed quickly by ultraviolet radiation from the sun. Ozone, O_3, an unstable form of oxygen, is produced when the more common oxygen molecule, O_2, absorbs ultraviolet radiation. Most of this action occurs in a thin layer near 35 kilometers. Some ultraviolet penetrates to lower levels and produces correspondingly weaker concentrations of ozone, but the bulk of ozone below the primary generation level is due largely to turbulent mixing and vertical air motion.

When an area of upward motion is produced by stratospheric winds, the rising mass replaces the ozone-rich upper layers with ozone-poor air from the low stratosphere. Consequently, the layers below the formation layer contain subnormal amounts of ozone, and a sharply marked level of maximum concentration is found near the top of the photochemically active layer. On the other hand, when air descends through the 35 kilometer level, ozone-rich air replaces normal air of the lower stratosphere, so that the column contains an above normal amount of ozone. In this case a deep layer with a nearly uniform concentration of ozone would be found in place of the sharp maximum in the ascending columns.

The ozone content of a given vertical column of air in the stratosphere is also influenced by horizontal motion. For example, different winds at various levels make it possible for one layer of ozone to move in beneath another higher layer. In such a case a double maximum of ozone could exist in a single vertical column of air.

Within the last decade, meteorologists have found striking evidence that rapid heating occasionally occurs in restricted regions of the stratosphere. This heating, closely connected with ozone concentrations, may have profound influence on the subsequent weather at lower levels.

Experiments are now being devised to measure ozone concentrations from satellites. The technique takes advantage of the ability of ozone to absorb portions of the sun's ultraviolet radiation. Radiation absorption will be measured at different slant ranges through the atmosphere between the sun and the satellite. This can be done when the instrument is in a position to look at the sun along a line nearly parallel to the earth's surface. As the satellite moves toward the dark side of the earth, the line of view to the sun is first through the high stratosphere, then through lower and lower layers as shown in Figure

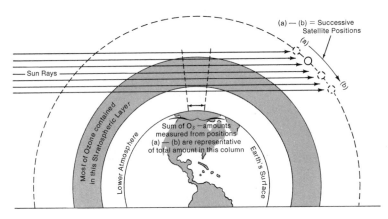

Figure 7.1 Schematic sketch of a method of measuring the concentration of ozone in the stratosphere by viewing the sun through lowering paths in the atmosphere, as satellite moves from *(a)* to *(b)*.

7.1. The ozone content along each of these paths can be deduced by comparing radiation at frequencies where ozone is an efficient absorber, with radiation at frequencies where ozone is a less effective absorber.

Ozone measurements may prove to be the only means of deducing air motions at these altitudes because moisture is very scarce. The consequent lack of cloudiness precludes sensing in the visible but ozone is a substance that might be traced by measuring the shorter wavelengths.

Precipitation and thunderstorms are readily detected at large distances by ground-based radar and sferics equipment.* Radar signals are reflected from water droplets, and the returned signal reveals the position and, to some extent, the quantity of water contained in the droplets. Sferics equipment detects the long-wave radiation from lightning and similar discharges from convective clouds. Distance to the storm is not deducible from a single sferics station.

Both of these instrumental techniques, developed during and since World War II, are in routine use. Their adaptation for a satellite-borne system is in the design stage. Experiments will probably be flown during the Nimbus program.

While there is now routine use of ground-based weather radar and sferics equipment, flying the instruments on a satellite is not a simple matter. The wavelengths of the radiation involved are very long compared to the wavelength of infrared radiation. Most infrared radiation is emitted from the earth and its atmosphere at wavelengths shorter than 30 microns, while a *short* wavelength in the radar band is 3 centimeters—1,000 times longer! Lightning and similar electrical discharges will probably be detected most efficiently in the wavelength interval from 50 to 300 centimeters, which is some 100 times longer than the radar waves.

An important difficulty associated with detecting long wavelengths from satellites is that the sensors, in this case the antennae, must be proportionately larger than those used to detect shorter wavelengths. Greater size means greater weight and greater mechanical complexity. For example, the radar antenna will probably have to be erected in space, because it is too large to launch in its fully extended shape. Radar requires a parabolic antenna, similar to the type seen in microwave relay towers or those scanning about on an airport traffic control

* These are detectors which sense discharges of atmospheric electricity.

radar tower. One method suggested for erecting an antenna in orbit is to inflate a plastic envelope of the proper shape. Manufacturing such a device with the required rigidity and precision would require a major engineering effort.

Antennae for sferics signals need not be so complicated because, unlike radar which transmits and receives a highly directional beam, the sferics antenna can be nondirectional and need not transmit energy. The sferics receiver, essentially a radio receiver, can be made sensitive to a swath a few hundred miles wide beneath the satellite. In order to determine from which part of the area the sferics emanated, it would be necessary to correlate the signals with the most well-developed clouds on concurrent television pictures or infrared patterns.

Sferics data are valuable because the energy originates in convective clouds. This type of cloud plays an important role in transporting heat and moisture into the upper troposphere. By this mechanism the sun's radiation is converted into the internal energy of the atmosphere.

Radar detection of precipitation (and the rain-producing clouds) is more complex to adapt to satellites. The difficulty arises because the radar set transmits a pulsed signal that is reflected from the target (water droplets) back to the radar receiver. By comparing the phase of the outgoing signal with that of the incoming one, the distance to the target is derived. The density of the water drop concentration is gauged from the intensity of the returned signal. This complex system requires delicate adjustment which would be difficult to maintain on a satellite in orbit. Perhaps satellite radar will be completely practical only when a man is present in the satellite to operate the equipment.

A system capable of *delivering data directly to remote users* will be especially important for short-range forecasting. National weather centers at great distances from the satellite data center, as well as ships at sea and other mobile units, must depend upon long communication lines and suffer the consequent delays. The forecast period may expire before satellite data arrive. These delays will be shorter when communications satellites are fully developed, but a direct read-out satellite is a more straightforward solution. Furthermore, short-range forecasts (up to several hours) depends not at all upon conditions on the other side of the world, but only upon detailed conditions of the surrounding several hundred miles. For these reasons, a direct read-out system that produces data for the area surrounding the receiver will fill a vital requirement.

The first experiment conducted with this idea in mind was the Automatic Picture Transmission (APT) television first flown on TIROS VIII and Nimbus, but infrared data must be transmitted in the same way as the APT picture signals to provide economical data twice each day. The direct read-out infrared (DRIR) feature of the TOS system will accomplish this. DRIR will be a read-out of HRIR through the APT system during the night part of the orbit. So the inexpensive APT ground station will receive the high resolution pictures as the satellite passes over it in the daytime and the less clearly defined but highly informative infrared "pictures" as the satellite passes over the station during the night.

The instruments just described are by no means the only equipment that can be used to obtain meteorological data. An important part of the electromagnetic spectrum which has not yet been exploited is the microwave region that lies just below radar wavelengths. It is known that various types of surfaces on the earth and gases in the atmosphere radiate at microwave frequencies. For example, atmopheric oxygen radiates near 0.5 centimeters (5,000 microns), and some terrain radiates near 0.1 centimeters.

Oxygen radiates at different intensities at various wavelengths near 0.5 centimeters, but its specific radiation characteristics are not known. Once the radiating characteristics of oxygen are completely known, it is possible that lines and bands in this vicinity can be used as a thermal probe of the atmosphere. This technique might extend our sensing down to layers which cannot be accurately measured by infrared radiometers in the 15-micron carbon dioxide band.

The maximum intensity of microwave emissions from different substances occurs at different wavelengths. Sensing the wavelength at which this maximum occurs might then be a means of identifying the emitting substance. Sea ice emits quite differently than sea water; a swarm of locusts will look noticeably different from the desert background to the microwave detector. Some of the microwaves can penetrate clouds and smoke, and so might be used to detect forest fires.

The use of microwave sensing awaits the completion of both theoretical and experimental studies. One difficulty in design is the relatively large antennae required. Many other important questions are yet to be answered. For example, the microwave radiating characteristics of many substances are not known. New snow emits at different microwave frequencies than old snow, but the extent of this difference is not known. Wind-roughened water emits differently from smooth water. Such a feature might be employed to detect sea roughness (and thus wind speed?), but the effect of ocean surface temperature on such measurements must be investigated.

Microwave emission, similar to infrared mission, is influenced by the temperature of the radiating surface. The effect of temperature in the microwave range is somewhat smaller than in the infrared. If, for example, two identical surfaces differed in temperature by $3°$, the infrared emission would differ by about 4 per cent while the microwave emission would differ by only about 1 per cent. These effects are important, since for some applications it might be necessary to derive effective radiating temperatures from microwave radiation. In such cases the relatively small effect of temperature on emission would make the interpretation of microwave data difficult.

The very short wavelengths below the visible have not been completely exploited. New techniques can be developed to utilize the visible spectrum as well as the ultraviolet. The methods mentioned in the remainder of this chapter are based on theory that must be extended before they can be applied.

The optical laser is a recent development that operates in the visible spectrum. This device produces pulsed, high energy, light waves that might be used as atmospheric probes. Dense clouds are quite opaque to laser beams, so an obvious application is to use laser pulses in the same manner as radar pulses to measure cloud height. Laser pulses might also measure the speed of motion of cloud elements by means of the Doppler shift* between transmitted and reflected pulses.

---

* The Doppler shift is the effect on frequency of a wave signal, due to motion of the signal source. A familiar example is the changing pitch of an automobile horn sounded as it passes rapidly. As the horn is approaching, the frequency (pitch) increases; as it recedes, the pitch lowers.

In the laser application, the satellite would transmit a pulsed light at a given frequency. After being reflected from a target such as a cloud, some of the pulsed energy would be returned to the satellite. If the distance between the cloud and the instrument were increasing, the reflected pulse would have a lower frequency than the transmitted pulse; if the target were approaching, the reflected pulse would have a higher frequency. A serious difficulty arises because a large part of the motion between the instrument and the cloud is caused by the motion of the satellite itself. The satellite speed may be thousands of miles per hour, while the typical target speed would be under 100 miles per hour. The measurements would have to be extremely accurate so that the relatively small cloud speed would be detectable. Nearly all the theory for such application is known, but, at present, technological difficulties are overwhelming.

Absorption by oxygen of the short, ultraviolet wavelengths has already been discussed in connection with ozone. Oxygen also absorbs solar energy near 0.78 microns, just on the boundary between the visible and the infrared. A large amount of solar radiation reaches the atmosphere at this wavelength, so this band may be relatively easy to measure. One suggested application is the determination of cloud height.

To make this determination, the energy reflected from cloud tops in the 0.78 micron band (a strong oxygen absorption band) would be compared with the energy at a nearby nonabsorbing band, say, at 0.80 microns. The difference between these energies would be proportional to the path length through oxygen from the satellite to the cloud top. Since distribution of oxygen in the vertical is known with sufficient accuracy, the vertical distance could be related to the amount of oxygen determined by the measured absorption.

Since cloud tops are not entirely opaque, some of the radiation at 0.78 microns can penetrate the upper layers of clouds and be multiple-reflected from droplet to droplet before it emerges from the cloud top and returns to the satellite. Such a complex path would, of course, be longer than the straight-line distance from the satellite to the clouds, so the measurement would yield an erroneously low cloud height. Research already underway will determine the magnitude of this effect.

Measurement of the *solar constant* is also important to meteorology. The solar constant is defined as the total amount of the sun's energy that reaches the "top of the atmosphere." Estimates of this energy, based on measurements made at the earth's surface, are essentially unchanging, thus the term solar "constant." Energy at very short wavelengths is absorbed high in the atmosphere by oxygen and ozone. For that reason there could be variations in the solar "constant" which are not detectable at the earth's surface. Variations in solar output could provide a variable heat source for the stratosphere which, in turn, might influence the circulation at lower levels. A satellite is the only means by which the total solar energy can be measured.

The difficulties in making satellite measurements of the solar constant are due mostly to the rigorous demands of stability and sensitivity of the instrument during a long period of operation. Extreme accuracy is needed because the variation will be small. Measurements will be meaningful only after records over long periods are available. This requires that the operation and calibration of the instrument be very stable. If some electrical components changed with age, it might cause a change of signal strength which could be interpreted as a variation in the solar constant. If the instrument accepted energy from a large part of the solar spectrum, energy variations in the short wavelengths would be an extremely small part of the total energy measured.

An alternate approach might be to measure energy only in the short wavelength ranges where the variation is expected to occur. The advantage of such a scheme would be that any variations in the shorter wavelengths would then be a large percentage variation of the portion measured.

At this time we do not know whether the solar constant variation is important or even exists. If it is significant, it would be important, for example, to long-range forecasting. If a successful experiment shows that there is no significant variation in the sun's output, the measurements could be terminated.

A vital question that affects meteorological analysis is, "What is the wind speed and direction?" This simple query is far from simple for the meteorological satellite to answer. How the array of cloud patterns can sometimes be used to estimate wind directions has already been discussed, but the complete answer is still lacking. Application of the Doppler shift, mentioned earlier, is an untested procedure insofar as satellite instrumentation is concerned. Direct measurement of the wind from satellites may depend upon sensing the motion of a tracer being carried along by the wind. The principal obstacles to this method fall into two classes: first is the matter of finding a satisfactory tracer; second is the great technical difficulty of identifying and then pinpointing the location of each of a large number of individual targets.

Although clouds are abundant, they continually grow and decay; consequently, they are poor tracers for long time intervals. They might be used as short interval tracers, but detecting cloud displacement during a short time interval is a stringent requirement. For examples, the normal cumulus cloud has a life cycle of 20 to 40 minutes. A wind of 30 knots would carry an individual cumulus cloud 15 nautical miles in 30 minutes. In order to determine this wind speed with an accuracy of $\pm$ 20 per cent, the cloud location would have to be determined to within $\pm$ 1.5 nautical miles at the beginning and end of that half-hour. Such accuracy cannot be anticipated with operational meteorological satellites.

Some cloud fields exist for long periods. TIROS pictures have shown patterns that exhibited little change when photographed 100 minutes apart, on successive passes. But the wind actually blows right through these larger-scale patterns. Consequently, the clouds do not move with the speed of the wind, so measuring their speed and direction would not yield the desired wind information.

Artificial tracers such as balloons are much more satisfactory for following actual air motion. A balloon made of a nonstretchable material can be slightly overinflated. Such a balloon would retain a fixed volume, and consequently would float at a level of constant density. Since vertical motions are usually very small, most balloons would remain at a predetermined level. Experiments of this kind have already been successfully conducted using earth-based tracking equipment. Placing the tracking equipment on a satellite would make possible the use of these constant level balloons to measure winds over the entire world.

The foregoing discussion of future meteorological satellites has ranged from experiments that will be in orbit as these words are being read, through rather speculative developments, some of which may never prove feasible. In addition, there are some meteorological variables for which measurements are desperately needed, but for which no techniques of measurement have yet been suggested. The most obvious of these is the accurate measurement of the atmospheric pressure at the earth's surface over the vast regions where barometers cannot be used routinely. Another is the need to measure the temperature of the air near the surface.

In principle, atmospheric pressure should be measurable because it is simply the weight (mass) of the total column of air from the satellite to the surface of the earth. Some method of detecting this total mass would provide a measurement of the surface pressure. The difficulty arises because it is the relatively small percentage variation in the pressure from point to point that is significant for meteorology. The average pressure at sea level is equivalent to the mass of 29.92 inches of mercury, but significant variations over a distance of 100 miles are as small as $\pm$ 0.05 inch—less than a fifth of one per cent. We are thus faced with the familiar problem of having to detect a very small difference between two very large quantities.

The temperature of the earth's surface has a very strong influence on the infrared radiation in the water vapor window, but measurement of that radiation cannot yield an *accurate* measurement of the surface temperature. Although in cloudless regions measurements in the window may provide reasonably good estimates of surface temperatures, water vapor in the air above the surface does radiate a small amount in this frequency interval. Therefore, deep humid layers in the atmosphere frequently prevent some of the surface radiation from reaching the satellite. In addition, nearly 40 per cent of the earth's surface is always cloud-covered, and clouds are almost totally opaque to radiation emitted from the earth's surface. At present, there does not appear to be any method of sensing the temperature beneath a heavy overcast.

In this chapter we have discussed the frontiers of development and the obstacles that must yet be overcome. In this way, the reader can appreciate both the vast potential of this new technology and the scientific challenges it presents. In a similar vein, our purpose has been to explain the manner in which satellite data can and are being applied to weather forecasting and research.

The invention of the barometer did not make the wind vane obsolete, nor did the development of radiosondes signal the closing of all other meteorological observing stations. Neither will the weather satellite replace the other sources of weather data.

It is important that the nature of this exciting advance be appreciated on its own merit rather than on the basis of uninformed enthusiasm. As a technical achievement, meteorological satellites are impressive, but more significantly, they represent a fundamental and major advance in the techniques of measuring the atmosphere. These improved measurements will help us to understand our whole geophysical system of air, sea, and earth—a necessary step if man is to make his existence on this densely populated planet both comfortable and meaningful.

Basic Books for More Information

ADLER, IRVING. *Seeing the Earth from Space.* New York: The New American Library of World Literature, 1962.

LEHR, PAUL E., R. WILL BURNETT, and HERBERT S. ZIM. *Weather.* New York: Golden Press, 1957, 1965 (Golden Science Guide). 160 pp.

SUTTON, O. G. *The Challenge of the Atmosphere.* New York: Harper & Row, 1961. 227 pp.

VAETH, J. GORDON. *Weather Eyes in the Sky—America's Meteorological Satellites.* New York: The Ronald Press, 1965. 124 pp.

WIDGER, WILLIAM K., JR. *Meteorological Satellites.* New York: Holt, Rinehart & Winston, 1965. 276 pp.

Analysis, *See* Data processing; Cloud pictures

APT (Automatic Picture Transmission), *See* Television Systems; Cameras

Atmosphere
circulation of, 2–4
gases, 17

AVCS (Advanced Vidicon Camera System), *See* Cameras

Cameras, *See also* TIROS; Nimbus
angle of view, 23, 36, 37, 44, 47
APT, 37, 47, 112
AVCS, 36, 44
field of view, 23, 33, 36, 37, 44, 47
low light, 105
picture matrix, 23

Cloud pictures (television)
bands, 87
cellular cumulus, 75
cyclones, 2, 70–74, 84, 88–90
eddies, 91
hurricanes, 70–74, 88
interpretation of, 21, 83–91
jet streams, 74
mountain waves, 74, 76, 91
severe weather, 74, 75
vorticity, 87, 88

Clouds, *See also* Cloud pictures
cirrus, 9, 74
classification, 9
cumulus, 9, 21, 75
stratus, 9

Coriolis force, 4

Data processing
digital computer, 59, 83, 103–105
gridding, 58, 59
nephanalysis, 43, 55, 69
picture data, 43, 58, 59
presentation, 47, 105
sampling rates, 64, 105

Data transmission
acquisition range, 54, 55

bandwidth and frequencies, 20
command, 39
facsimile, 69
point to point, 43, 55, 69
satellite to ground, 20, 39, 55, 112
satellite relay of, 111, 112

DRIR (Direct Readout Infrared Radiometer), *See* Infrared

Electromagnetic Radiation, *See* Radiation

Energy in the atmosphere, 6, 7

ESSA (Environmental Science Services Administration), picture credits

Explorer satellites, 1, 30, 31

Forecasting, long-range, 96–98, 115

Ground stations, 39, 112

HRIR (High Resolution Infrared Radiometer), *See* Infrared; Radiation; Radiation sensors

Hurricanes, *See* Cloud pictures

Ice and snow, 69, 77, 106

Infrared, *See also* Radiation; Radiation sensors
DRIR, 112
HRIR, 44, 47, 82, 83
intensity, 93, 94
mapping, 31–33, 76, 77, 94, 95
MRIR, 62–64
water vapor window, 17, 18, 79, 94

Kinescope, 41

Laser, 113

Meteorological sensors, *See* Weather observation

Nephanalysis, 43, 55, 69; *See also* Data processing

Nimbus, 33, 43, 44, 83

Operational requirements, 100–103
Orbits of satellites
  earth-synchronous, 103
  equatorial, 103
  heights, 23, 24, 28, 103
  inclination, 21, 37, 44
  orbital plane, 26, 27
  polar, 26
  precession, 40
  prograde, 37
  retrograde, 44
  sun-synchronous, 51, 68, 103
Ozone measurement, 108, 109

Pictures, television, *See also* Cloud
    pictures
  field of view, 23, 24
  photogrammetry, 55, 57–59
  picture matrix, 23
  resolution, 19, 19n., 24
  storage on satellite, 39
Pioneer I, II, 31

Radiation, *See also* Infrared
  atmospheric absorption, 17
  carbon dioxide, 107
  earth-atmosphere system, 17, 95
  electromagnetic, 14, 15
  emission, 18, 107
  heat budget, 17, 95
  microwave, 14, 112, 113
  solar, 15, 17
  temperatures, 17, 112, 113
  terrestrial, 18
  ultraviolet, 15, 108, 109
  wavelengths, 14, 15, 31, 93–95, 107,
    108
Radiation sensors, *See also* Infrared
  angle of view, 26
  description of sensors, 31, 61, 77, 98,
    107
  direct readout of HRIR, 112
  field of view, 26, 47, 63
  high resolution radiometer (HRIR),
    44, 47, 82, 83, 105, 106, 112
  infrared spectrometer, 77, 98
  medium resolution radiometer
    (MRIR), 62–64
  oxygen absorption spectrometer, 114

Solar constant, 115
Sputnik I, 1

Television systems, *See also* TIROS;
    Cameras
  APT, 35, 47, 112
  AVCS, 36
  kinescope, 41
  tape recorders, 39
  vidicon, 19, 33, 35, 36
Temperature, *See also* Radiation; In-
    frared
  Kelvin scale, 17n.
  mapping, 31, 47, 76, 77
  measurement, 14
  microwave, 112, 113
TIREC project, 69; *See also* Ice and
    snow
TIROS
  acronym, 11
  cameras, 19, 33, 35–37
  launch, 2, 33, 51
  lifetime, 33
  operation, 39
  orbit, *See* Orbits of satellites
  power, 35
  spacecraft description, 35
  stabilization, 37
  TIROS, 2, 11, 33, 37–41, 47, 68–70
  TOS system, 43, 47, 51
  wheel, 33, 51
TOS (*TIROS Operational Satellite*),
    See TIROS

Vanguard II, 29
Vidicon, *See* Television systems

Weather observation
  conventional, 7–10
  networks, 7–9
  radiosonde, 10
  radar, 10, 110
  rocket, 11
  satellites, *See* TIROS; Nimbus
  sferics, 110, 111
Wind measurement from satellites, 113,
    116
Winds, zonal, 4–6